YOU CAN Run

Pain Free!

A physio's 5 step
guide to enjoying
injury-free and
faster running

BRAD BEER

What others are saying ...

As a professional athlete, the ability to run pain and injury free has been critical to my performance. At last Brad has distilled the same principles he has used to help me run pain free over my career into a resource available to runners of all levels. If you have an interest in exploring your running potential, read this book.

Shannon Eckstein, Ironman legend (eight times winner Nutri-Grain Series, five times World Ironman, six times Australian Ironman champion)

I am thrilled that Brad has written a book that will truly enhance all athletes' ability to stay healthy and injury free. I have such great respect for Bard and his practices and philosophies. He has helped some of my athletes get back to running quicker and more effectively than any other physio ever has. Not only this, but with Brad's help, and the help of this book, I plan also on these athletes staying injury free throughout the year, and year after year!

Siri Lindley, former world triathlon champion and Olympic triathlon coach

At the APA, we live by the mantra, 'Move well, stay well'. Australian physiotherapists are well equipped to help the community stay physically active at all levels. Brad's book serves this function by debunking the myths that prohibit many people from running for fitness.

Cris Massis, CEO Australian Physiotherapy Association

Brad's passion for running and zeal to help others shine through every page of his new book. This work is underpinned by sound biomechanical and physiological principles, all written in his easy to follow, inimitable style. Thoroughly recommended.

Dr Ralph Vida MBBS (HONS) (Ad.) FRACGP

As a GP for more than 30 years, a long-time runner and a self-referred client of Brad's, I can attest to his knowledge, enthusiasm and positive approach to the injured runner. He understands the goal is to return to running – not change to walking or take up another sport! Brad's methods helped me to achieve a successful return to running after injury.

Dr Dianne Nichol MBBS (HONS) (QLD) FRACGP

Brad's passion for and knowledge of both running and physiotherapy is evident in this book. Any runner will find it of great benefit in their quest for injury-free and faster running.

Emma Moffatt, dual Australian Olympian and world champion triathlete

It never ceases to amaze me how quickly I'm on the road to recovery or just generally tuned up every time I see Brad. I often say, 'he is a genius!'

Mat Rogers, dual Australian rugby representative

The combination of Brad's passion, knowledge and clinical experience in all things running makes this book a must-read and valuable resource for runners of all ages and experience levels.

Steven Obst, physiotherapist and PhD candidate, Griffith University

Brad is a high-performance physiotherapist and his insights about running well and running fast have been gained through both personal experience and treating some of the world's leading athletes over many years. This is a must-read for any runner – from beginner to professional – with simple and highly effective strategies to help you achieve your running personal best, injury free.

Dr Hal Rice MBBS (UQ) FRANZCR, MRI imaging specialist, Associate Professor Griffith University and Bond School of Medicine, and sub 2:40 marathoner

Authentic and honest, Brad is a health professional who lives and breathes in a runner's body. Long may you run, Brad – you and your readers.

Peter Hall 140,000 k and still going, and proprietor NIKE Robina

Brad's five step method is a proven way of beating running injuries. This book really does unlock the 'secrets' to running pain and injury free!

Hayley Bateup, professional Ironwoman and three times Coolangatta Gold champion

As a trail runner and age-group triathlete, I've had many niggles that have threatened my running career. But Brad's expert knowledge of human physiology and running mechanics has seen him diagnose and rehabilitate even the most obscure problem. He knows his stuff! These five steps will keep the injuries at bay and improve your speed but, best of all, they will see you spending less time at the physio and more time on the trails. Physio Brad has done himself out of a job!

John FitzGerald, trail runner, age-group triathlete

In just five months, I've gone from zero to cruising through my first 21 km (injury free)! Without Brad, this feat would have been insurmountable, but Brad's five step method has made the impossible, dare I say it, absolutely enjoyable!

Rev Ralph Mayhew, pastor at Newlife Uniting Church

Brad has helped me with ankle and calf injuries. Brad is sincere, extremely encouraging, knowledgeable, and an expert in his field. Brad's running workshops are first class and a must-do for all types of runners. It has revolutionised the way I run.

Chris Hassell, runner

After two years of not being able to run at all due to plica syndrome in both knees, Brad had me up and running again within weeks, and totally without pain or injury. By following Brad's exercise plan, I'm running regularly and doing all the training I previously enjoyed. I am still amazed at the speed of my recovery and feel truly grateful to have met Brad.

Lesley Odisho, psychology student

I've never met anyone else with such professional enthusiasm to help others return to the activities that they love. Brads energetic passion is contagious, leaving no stone unturned in his pursuit of excellence.

Graeme Rundle, personal trainer

Having suffered the runner's 'bust' that Brad aptly describes in his book, I'm delighted that his advice and care have returned me to running with renewed confidence so quickly.

Sheree Young, GM and co-owner, Body Science International

I was on the brink of giving up on my running ambitions until Brad reassured me that he could restore my dream if I followed the recommendations he provided during treatment sessions. I have come so far … from being able to jog for only two minutes (due to an ITB band injury) to now competing in the 10 km at University Games. Thanks Brad for getting me back on track!!!

Joshua-Kaleb Faulkner, runner and university student

As an ageing recreational runner and competitive squash player, it's all about injury management for me. Brad has helped me recover quickly from an annoying knee strain that I'd been struggling with for some time. I'm glad I recently switched to the 'guru'. He understands runners and their injuries better than any other health professional I've been to in the past.

Martin Simpkins, runner

While training for my first marathon, Brad not only treated and repaired an injury I got, but he also gave me an exercise and running plan to ensure it didn't recur and I was 'strong' enough to handle the heavy work load. I made it thanks to Brad! It will be refreshing to read an educated and informative book written by an Australian, a runner, and an expert in his field.

Travis Ireland, Director Corporate Challenge Events

As an age group 55+ triathlete, I would often struggle with the run leg due to injury. Due to Brad's guidance, physiotherapy skills and recommended exercises, I now love to run pain free. I'm sure I'll be running for many more years to come. Thanks Brad.

Janette Lindores, triathlete and runner

Keeping fit and healthy by running is essential for me in my life at work and at home. When injury has hit, Brad's experience, expert advice and excellent treatment has put me back on the road, faster than I expected.

Stuart Quarterman, Baptist pastor

Working in a busy gym, I come into contact with many people carrying injuries, and facing possible surgery. My first suggestion to them is to go and see Brad at Pogo Physio. Brad will assess the problem and why it's occurring, and get you on the road to recovery without the downtime. Brad has also treated many of my running and various other injuries over the past several years. No matter what injury I confront Brad with, he always gets me back training without unnecessary downtime, exceeding my expectation every time.

Jenny Hocken, personal trainer

Brad Beer is an absolutely excellent physiotherapist who has always provided me with an amazing professional and friendly service. He knows how to work with each individual's body to strengthen muscles and eliminate pain.

Daniel Coleman, professional triathlete

When looking to overcome a running injury, there is no better physio to see than one with an elite running background. Brad's knowledge and 'layman's' explanation of what is wrong and how he can fix it puts your mind to rest during your first consultation.

Paul Knight, runner

Having spent the last sixteen years being a professional athlete, I can honestly say I have had the results Brad has given me; the man is the body messiah!

Nick Gates, Cycling Management, former Tour de France competitor & professional cyclist

Brad has kept me going through various injuries such as plantar fasciitis and Achilles injuries. He always gets me back on my feet and going again. I would not still be going without him!

Christine Manning, triathlete

Brad helped me with a hamstring problem that lingered for three years. It has now been addressed with proper treatment, exercises and care. I'm so happy!

Karin Jackson, triathlete and runner

Returning to running fitness after injury can be a long road but with Brad's experience and expertise at least you know it's a sure thing.

Dr Sam Jones, veterinarian and runner

Utilising the exercises contained within this book I was able to go from not being able to walk downstairs without severe knee pain to being back in full training in only four weeks. Thanks Brad.

Luke McDonald, CEO Community Services Institute of Training

As an orthopaedic surgeon specialising in knee surgery, it's clear running technique plays a vital role in injury prevention. Brad's 5 Step logical approach to avoiding and correcting the multifactorial causes of repetitive running injuries is a fantastic resource for Runner's of all levels and ages.

Christopher Vertullo MBBS, FRACS, FAOrthA, Director Knee Research Australia, Adjunct Assoc Professor, Centre for Musculoskeletal Research Griffith University

Acknowledgements

*I want to acknowledge the following people for their support
in making what you hold in your hand possible.*

To my precious wife Cristina, thank you for your endless
love and support, your belief in me, your sacrifice, and your
patience and steadfastness as we journey this life together.

To my beautiful daughter Isabella, you bring so much
joy. I am eternally blessed to be your earthly father.

To my wonderful parents Margaret and Arthur, thank you
for your many years of sacrifice, love, and support.

To my beautiful sister Belinda, thank you, for always being in
my corner, for the wins, troughs, and everything in between.

To our families' much loved Ian, who we lost during the
writing of this manuscript. Thank you for touching all our
lives, and for reminding us of life's many simple pleasures.

To my extended Portugese family, thank you for the use of the family
biblioteca in Gandara during the writing of this manuscript.

To my team at POGO, who have patiently endured this project, thank
you for being a constant source of encouragement and inspiration.

To the KPI Australia team: Glen Carlson, Daniel
Priestley, and Andrew Griffiths. Thank you for helping
me 'unpack' the knowledge that was second nature to me,
and 'repackage' it so that it can now serve many.

To my editor Charlotte, and publishing aficionado Michael
Hanrahan, thank you for your patience, expertise, and
guidance in seeing this project through to completion.

To my dear friend Mark, your story, your overcoming, and the
role that your running fitness played, have forever opened my
eyes to the importance of maintaining optimal physical health.

Finally, to my own Heavenly Father for the revelation
to not leave one's legacy but rather to live it.

Dedication

This book is dedicated to the thousands of runners who throughout my career have trusted me with their physical health and performance.

It has been my great pleasure to have helped you unlock your true running potential. May you continue to enjoy life-long pain and injury free running.

Run on.

*May your running add life to your years
and years to your life.*

First published in 2015 by Brad Beer
www.bradbeer.com.au
www.pogophysio.com.au

National Library of Australia Cataloguing-in-Publication entry:

Creator:	Beer, Brad, author.
Title:	You can run pain free!: a physio's 5 step guide to enjoying injury-free and faster running / Brad Beer.
ISBN:	9780992529505 (paperback)
Subjects:	Running injuries – Prevention.
	Pain – Prevention.
Dewey Number:	613.7172

Cover design by Peter Reardon
Internal design and book production by Michael Hanrahan Publishing
Printed in Australia by McPherson's Printing

Contents

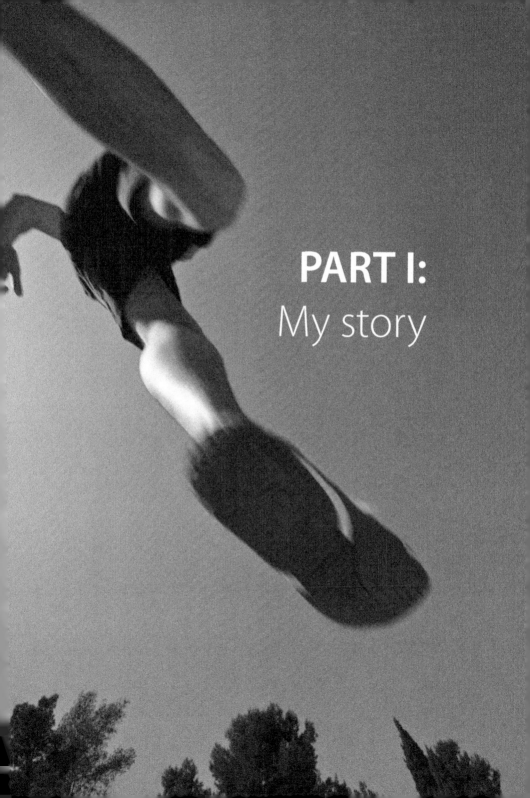

PART I:

My story

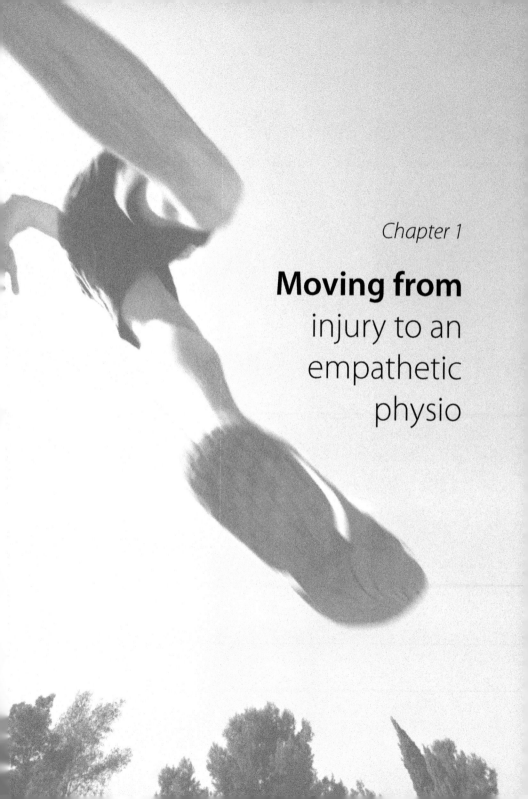

Chapter 1

Moving from
injury to an
empathetic
physio

An injury-laden youth

My first recollection of being awestruck by someone running was when I was 12 years of age. I was in front of the television watching the Tooheys Blue Triathlon Series. This series, which started in 1992 and ran for the better part of eight years, had exploded onto the triathlon scene in Australia and captured the imagination and interest of the sport-loving nation. In later years, the series would become the St George Triathlon Series, before its last iteration as the Accenture Triathlon Series.

In those early days, the triathlete I was most enamoured with was Brad Beven. Brad was a multiple Australian and World Series Triathlon Champion. He was an all-rounded and highly gifted athlete. And he had a cool nickname – 'the croc' – because, growing up in Far North Queensland, he used to complete his swim training in a creek that was home to a large crocodile. I would sit transfixed as I watched Brad lead from the front in the majority of races that comprised each round of the multi-round series. The races were normally short and very fast and, therefore, full of excitement and drama.

Brad attacked races at every chance he got, claiming victory after victory and back-to-back series titles. Brad's run leg was blistering fast; however, it was his unrelenting intention to win every contest that made watching this great athlete so exciting.

Brad's dominance in this series cemented him firmly as one of Australia's favourite sporting heroes. He was certainly mine.

The viewing of the series and my desire to be 'the next Brad Beven' had me hooked on the sport of triathlon. I had found a childhood hero who I earnestly wanted to emulate. Over the next seven years, when asked by career teachers and well-meaning adults what career path I wanted to take, I told all of them that I was going to be a professional triathlete.

Could I even make a living from it? Was it even a sustainable lifestyle? I didn't know. I certainly hadn't researched the life of a professional triathlete to determine if it was even viable. I simply loved the sport. My sole intention was to emulate the feats of my childhood sporting hero, Brad Beven. I saw the first step of reaching Beven's heights as becoming a professional triathlete.

Fortunately for me, my ambition was bolstered by some natural talent for endurance sport. I performed well at school cross country and swimming carnivals, rode a bike well in local cycling road races, and even went on to make state representative triathlon teams. My dream of becoming a professional triathlete seemed to have some merit – I seemed to be laying the groundwork for making this my career.

Even as an adolescent I knew that in order for my dream of becoming a professional triathlete to become a reality I needed to be focused and committed to training. Fortunately, along with my natural ability, I did not lack ambition, motivation or self-discipline. I had no trouble getting up early on the sub-zero winter mornings that were common in Grafton, the country town I grew up in. Nor did I mind walking through freezing cold paddocks to get to the main road so I could get a lift from a fellow swimmer's father to go to swim training at the local indoor pool.

My progress toward achieving my goal of becoming a 'pro-triathlete' was not to be derailed by the cold mornings or early training sessions, or by the lack of commitment that derailed so many promising junior sporting careers. Instead, the greatest difficulty I experienced as an aspiring junior triathlete was the frustrating challenge of recurring and excessive running-related injuries.

Fortunately, I was training for triathlon – the run leg was only one part of a race and my bike and swim legs remained relatively injury-free. This allowed me to log plenty of work on the bike, and in the pool, which kept me fit. My running training, on the other hand, was plagued with a seemingly never-ending string of running-related injuries. It seemed like I was always injured! I was regularly sitting out running training sessions and, at best, my running training sessions were modified, which at least allowed me to maintain some degree of 'running' fitness.

Arriving at a defining life question

At the age of 14, just 24 months into the pursuit of my life dream of becoming a professional triathlete I was already beset by injury. My local running coach recommended I see a highly regarded physiotherapist with the hope of getting my injured body 'back on track'. The physio my coach recommended lived over 200 kilometres north of my hometown, and her name was

Suzanne. Suzanne's expertise and the high recommendation my coach had given her meant the distance was overlooked. Making the long return drive to Ballina in order to see Suzanne became an almost weekly ritual.

My injuries were a combination of the most frequently experienced adolescent sports-related injuries. I experienced Osgood-Schlatter disease in both of my knees, Sever's disease around my heel and Achilles, and a recurringly sore and stiff lower back. In addition, I also incurred many running-specific injuries including: ITB friction syndrome, plantar fasciitis, and some hip-related problems and pains.

As well as my numerous sports injuries, I was involved in various crashes off my bike that occurred either while training or during races. These bike crashes added to the number of long drives to receive Suzanne's physio treatments. However, the long drives and necessary compliance with the prescribed home physio exercises that Suzanne would set were an easy sacrifice to make. I was so focused on chasing my professional triathlon career. Nothing was going to stop me. Not even my growing injury list.

Meanwhile, at the training track, my many adolescent injuries resulted in a modified running program. My running coach, Terry, a retiring school teacher, would have me water running and doing running drills while the other non-injured athletes would run. One afternoon I can recall doing 3 kilometres of a walking high-knee drill while the other athletes looked quizzically at my peculiar training session.

The modifications kept me training, but not at the peak running level that I required. My inability to complete the required running training affected my performance during the run leg in the junior triathlon races that I was regularly competing in. It became very common for me to lead a triathlon event after the bike leg of the race, only to fade on the run leg. I was used to getting passed by other competitors on the run leg and battling on trying to retain a podium finish. If unsuccessful, I would regularly be relegated out of the podium places and into the minor placings.

My running ability became a point of anxiety for me, and cast doubts in my mind as to whether I really 'had what it took' to be a professional triathlete. At one point, the multitude of injuries I suffered got me very down emotionally. I recall my caring mum trying her best to console me after one particular disappointing school cross country result. I was 15 years of age and I was sitting on my bed with tears welling up in my eyes. My mum said, 'Maybe you are just not made to be a runner, Brad. You can't be good at everything.' I was devastated at the thought that maybe Mum was right. Maybe I didn't have the running ability I would need to succeed as a professional triathlete. Many questions arose as I sat there on my bed with the tears flowing.

My concerns about the possible mismatch between my running ability and my sporting aspirations continued to grow. My mother's words echoed loudly. Did I actually have what it took to be a professional athlete? Would I ever be able to improve my run leg? Maybe I wasn't meant to be a runner? Perhaps my strengths lay elsewhere? Should I choose another sport? Maybe just stick with cycling?

I had begun to loathe the run leg of the triathlon and running training. Running had become my nemesis, my

'Achilles heel', and a point of almost embarrassment. I had little confidence in my running ability.

I recall many nights trying to get to sleep. I would lay there wondering whether I would always struggle with my run leg. I remember the disenchantment I felt when I pondered whether persisting on with trying to run pain and injury free was worth it. Was my body actually ever going to be able to run pain and injury free?

Becoming a physio who understands injured runners

Fast-forward to my career as a physiotherapist and I now treat scores of injured runners. In many of my injured running clients I see the same state of despondency that I felt as a young teen sitting on my bed. Just as I felt disheartened, and pondered the merits of persisting on with running and trying to run pain and injury free, so too are the musings of the vast majority of the injured running clients I consult.

Through my own experiences, I have developed an ability to empathise with the injured runner's disappointment, and the weight of emotion that this disappointment brings. This ability to empathise serves me well. My understanding of how the injured runner feels allows me to connect at a 'visceral' or 'gut' level. This connection is extremely beneficial in developing trust with the injured runner. Their knowing that they are working with someone who truly understands not just their condition but also their mindset is comforting.

I know the anxieties created by not being able to run due to injury. These are not only the short-term anxieties about loss of fitness and weight gain, but also the longer-term fears about not being able to do the thing that the injured runner loves to do – run. This understanding borne of my own experiences allows me to be more than just clinically effective. I have found that injured runners like to know that their feelings about their injury are acknowledged and, most importantly, that I as the therapist understand how they are feeling.

The question I arrived at as a teenager – 'Is it possible for me to run pain and injury free?' – is the core question that so many injured runners seek an answer to. Yet so many injured runners find it difficult to acknowledge that this is the very question that concerns them the most. Few runners voice such a question. Rather they 'park' it in their brain as a question that they will seek their own answers for. Their quest for answers will often be via their own experiences in overcoming their injuries, their own research, and the information and experiences they can glean from other like-minded and challenged runners. But more help is available.

The five step method that you will discover through reading this book will guide you towards experiencing pain- and injury-free running. The five steps will help you to unlock your true running potential.

Finally beating my injuries

In my final year of high school I was involved in a bike crash during a National Junior Triathlon championship race. My list of injuries was extensive: a fractured clavicle and scapula, subarachnoid brain haemorrhage, cartilage damage to the knee, and widespread contusions and skin damage. An extremely long and arduous physio rehabilitation ensued, as did a prolonged break from my triathlon and running training. A return to training was not possible until six months following the crash. Even then the best I could manage was a partial return to training. A full return to training was not possible due to my many injuries.

After finishing high school and slowly getting back into my training, I moved to the Gold Coast four hours north of my country hometown. My motivation for moving was to train with Bill, a highly regarded triathlon coach. It was the year 2000 and triathlon was soon to make its debut at the 2000 Sydney Olympic Games. In Bill's training squad was Craig Walton – one of the male triathletes representing Australia at the Olympics. I was in my element, as Craig Walton, just like Brad Beven, was a triathlon hero of mine.

That same year I started an exercise science degree at university. However, even after a prolonged break, extensive physio rehabilitation, and a gradual return to training, my attempts to train were frustrated by pain and post-crash residual injuries. I was still in pain as a result of the injuries incurred from the bike crash one year earlier. I was frustrated with the pain and my inability to progress. Bill, my coach, suggested I take a year out from triathlon training to allow my body to hopefully heal and 'settle down', and focus on university studies. I was emotionally torn about taking the break. I was fearful of taking time out and the associated opportunity cost it may carry. On the other hand, I was tired. I was sick of the pain and discomfort and limitations involved with not being able to do what I loved to do. I was also frustrated, as I was doing everything I knew to do and had been advised to do with no breakthrough. Reluctantly, I agreed to the break.

My one-year break from triathlon training, however, became many more years. An injury legacy from my bike crash that I later became aware of was a deep and very painful catching pain in my left knee. I would experience this pain every time I attempted a squat, or even something as simple as walking down stairs.

A few years later, and three years into my five-year university degree, with my knee pain worsening, I elected to have knee surgery. The surgeon, a highly regarded knee surgeon, was surprised to find a large cartilage crack lining the groove of my femur (thigh bone). He performed surgery, 'patched it' to the best of his ability, and sent me off with instructions to manage the knee.

The surgery had involved a procedure whereby the unstable cartilage was essentially 'picked' at with a surgical tool that resembled an icepick. Just as you would chip away at an ice block with an icepick, the surgeon picked away at my cartilage crack. The hope was that this micro-trauma to the cartilage and bone would stimulate the growth of new cartilage. Given the nature of the injury, however, the surgeon was not as hopeful of a full resolution and successful outcome as I would have wished. He counselled me that because the cartilage had been so badly damaged, I needed to accept that my symptoms may never be fully resolved. His last instruction was to minimise the amount that I ran or, ideally, avoid running all together.

Over the two years that followed surgery I made many attempts to run; sadly, none of them were void of my knee pain. I grew despondent and mildly depressed. Fortunately, this time around I was distracted by the rigours of my university degree which was now an Exercise Science degree combined with Physiotherapy.

As my university and part-time work commitments escalated, I was in no immediate rush to return to training. I threw my physical energies into regular surfing and gym-based training. At 25 years of age, and after my multiple failed attempts at running throughout my university years, I eventually let go of my professional triathlon dream.

The relinquishing of my childhood professional triathlon dream was softened by my focus to graduate from university as a physiotherapist. I planned to work with injured triathletes, runners and other athletes who were experiencing the waves of emotions associated with being injured.

A personal and professional collision

My first experience in the physiotherapy industry was as an employed graduate working in private practice. I was squarely focused on the treatment and rehabilitation of sports injuries; however, I quickly grew disillusioned with the environment and culture of the practice where I was employed. So, within several months of graduating, I handed in my notice on my first physiotherapy job. And, within one month of resigning, I opened my own private practice – something that, though extremely exciting, demanded long days and enormous hours.

While I was busy building and developing my practice, with very little 'down time', my fitness and further attempts at pain-free running training took a back seat. Several years into the life of the practice, I accompanied my wife on my first holiday and break away from the practice – a trip to Portugal to visit my wife's family.

One of the purposes of this trip was for my wife to complete a required university medical placement with her father (a Portuguese doctor). While my wife spent the day at the hospital working with her father I was without transport, bored and stuck waiting for the end of the work day. To pass the time I decided to start doing some runs around the local town where my father-in-law lived. On one particular run I ran for an hour. To my surprise I experienced very little knee pain. At the time, I didn't know why; I was bewildered. I wondered whether my knee had settled down as a result of the surgery. Perhaps the cartilage had regenerated or stabilised as the surgeon had hoped for?

Knowing about human cartilage's inherently poor ability to regenerate or heal, I was sceptical that the surgery had worked. I contemplated the possibility of 'supernatural healing'. That's right, a miracle! Three years earlier I had followed my wife into a local Christian Church. There, I found a real and genuine faith in a Creator. As I tried to reconcile my knee's improvement in function I recalled a prayer I had prayed, where I had offered God to do whatever He wanted me to do in exchange for my knee being healed. There I was – so desperate for help, I was 'brokering a deal' with God!

Divine intervention or the result of surgery, either way it seemed too good to be true – all I knew at that point was that this was the longest run I had done for over five years. Pain-free running was not something I had been accustomed to since my triathlon bike crash, which was now some eight years prior. And the best part was that this initial pain-free run was followed by many others.

On returning to Australia I set about running longer runs, and even made a return to the occasional track running session. Still no pain! Buoyed by my newfound ability to once again run pain free, I did something that as a junior athlete I had never entertained; I entered my first marathon. I completed my debut marathon with relatively low running kilometres behind me – and, incidentally, missed my goal time of three hours by just 90 seconds. I was hooked!

It was during my training for my marathon debut that I began to research running technique. I quickly recognised that my running technique needed to improve. I implemented the best of the information about running technique that I had sourced during this 12-month period into my own running. The results were wonderful. I was running much faster as an adult runner than I had ever done as a junior triathlete. My 5-kilometre and 10-kilometre times were at a level that as a junior, I had not thought were possible for me.

Meanwhile, in my physiotherapy practice, I became increasingly aware that running technique was often a causative factor for running-related injuries. I observed the positive outcomes that resulted when my injured running clients were educated about the importance of running with good technique. The changes were conducive to not only injury-free running but also to faster running. In addition to reduced injury rates,

I was getting regular reports of faster running times from my clients. My clients were as happy with their running as I was with mine.

Running with my new-found awareness of good running technique, I entered many running events of varying distances. I set about improving my marathon personal best time. In the meantime, professionally I was developing a strong following of runners who were seeking answers to their bothersome running niggles and injuries. These injured runners had heard how my rehabilitation methods were helping injured runners get back to running. They had also heard that my rehabilitation methods were resulting in faster running.

Just as I had lost hope as an adolescent athlete, many of the injured runners I was seeing had also lost hope that they could once again run pain and injury free. They had resigned themselves to accepting that a degree of injury or pain was to be their norm. Having harboured that fear myself for many years, I easily related to their concerns. I empathised with their frustrations, fears and often times their embarrassment. Injured runners quite commonly can feel a degree of embarrassment that something so seemingly 'trivial' as not being able to run could have them feeling so emotionally low.

Most times the injured runner would say things like, 'I shouldn't be so worried about this but ...', or 'I can't believe this upsets me so much − after all it's just running', or 'I've given up hope. I think I might concentrate on something other than running like cycling'. These statements pointed to a cry for answers. They also indicated the high value that being able to run without pain or injury was to the individual.

I was also fast discovering the joys and challenges of rehabilitating injured runners – witnessing formerly injury-plagued runners returning to pain- and injury-free running and also to happiness and emotional normality.

Typically, the rehabilitation process would commence with breaking the myth that injury is an inevitable part of a runner's life. As soon as hope that it was possible to run pain and injury free was restored for the injured runner, the platform was established for the treatment that would follow.

Refining my physio approach

Over the successive years in professional practice, I have continually refined my running injury rehabilitation approach. As word of mouth of my successes in rehabilitating injured runners has spread, I have guided thousands of runners back to pain- and injury-free and, ultimately, faster running.

This book is an articulation of my ideas and the five step methodology that I have refined through these years of working with injured runners. I repeatedly share the steps contained herein with my clients, and educate them on their best execution of the five steps. My five step method has helped runners of all ages and abilities – from the beginner runner or the runner taking on a longer distance challenge, the recreational, several times a week jogger, through to the elite and professional athlete.

I have found great pleasure in observing that, when all five steps of my five step method are implemented by injured runners, the injured runner will go on to experience the great joy and associated health benefits of running pain and injury free.

It is important to note that the five steps work in concert. If one of the five steps is left out, the runner's likelihood of achieving sustained pain- and injury-free running will be compromised. Leaving out one of the steps is akin to leaving a vital ingredient out of a cake mix. You wouldn't expect the cake to bake well, and nor can a runner expect a complete result if one of the five steps is overlooked or not addressed in full.

I believe that every runner, no matter what age, body shape or ability level, can and should experience pain- and injury-free running. I also believe that if more people were able to experience the uncomplicated joy and life-giving benefits that running provides, the happier and healthier the world would ultimately be.

Chapter 2

Why this book?

Among many runners is a shared belief that it is really not possible to run pain and injury free – a belief that if you run far enough and for long enough injury will be the inevitable result. Sadly many runners believe and wrongfully accept that succumbing to injury must be a normal part of the running experience. This is an often unspoken and deeply held belief that most runners would not openly express.

My aim in writing this book is to denounce this unfounded but widely held belief, and to reveal that it is possible to run pain and injury free.

Just as every golfer wants an improved golf game, so too every runner wants to run faster. One of the great thrills of seeing runners break free from their limiting injury beliefs is seeing them also go on to post personal best running times. Getting faster is a terrific by-product of not getting injured.

If you have lost hope that running pain and injury free is achievable and you have picked up this book, you must read on. I have written this book to answer the very question that I believe every injured runner at some point asks themselves: is it possible to run pain and injury free? I believe I have an answer.

Enjoy the discovery process.

Who is this book for?

While this book is targeted at the runner who wonders or has wondered if it is truly possible to run pain and injury free, this book is also written for any runner who:

> is seeking to proactively prevent injuries

> is currently injured and looking to return to running

> has been previously injured and never made a return to running

> is not concerned about injury prevention or rehabilitation but just wants to get faster.

Several categories of runners will also specifically benefit from this book. These include:

> beginner runners who are just getting started

> beginner runners who are training for their first event

> female runners who are discovering the simplistic joys of running while juggling home and family responsibilities

> seasoned runners who cannot get rid of a lingering injury

> runners looking to 'upsize' their challenge – for example, the runner who has a goal to upgrade from a half marathon distance race to a full marathon

> runners who suffer from emotional lows when injury keeps them from training or competing.

Getting the most out of this book

When reading this book for the first time I recommend reading it sequentially. If a particular section or chapter immediately grabs your attention, do your best to fight the temptation to start there, and instead start from the first chapter.

Each of the five steps builds on the previous step. While it isn't necessary to master each of the five steps before moving on to the next step, it is important that you attempt to put what you learn with each step into practice as you go.

My five step method of running pain and injury free is illustrated in the following figure.

I encourage you to get physical with this book. If a particular idea or point resonates with you, mark the book and date it.

Don't be shy to take a pen or a highlighter to pages. A well-read book is a book with marks! Making notes and highlighting key points will prove useful when you are getting ready to implement the ideas.

Good luck with your reading and running and, most importantly, the implementation of what you learn. In the words of Bruce Lee:

> Knowing is not enough, we must apply. Willing is not enough, we must do.

Finally, don't forget to not take your running too seriously. Remember to have daily fun!

PART II:
Boom and
busted

Chapter 3

Running
into injury

The second running boom

Fun runs have exploded and competitor field limits for these runs are routinely over-subscribed. Footpaths are more congested. Fluoro-coloured running shoes are everywhere to be seen. Running Lycra graces local cafes and coffee shops. Running shoes are no longer just reserved for use when running, they can be the perfect accessory to an outfit.

The rise of running's popularity is in full swing. The last decade has seen a relative explosion in people's interest in running. The sport's simplistic charms are being discovered and embraced by millions of people worldwide. So large is the increase in participation that trend analysts have termed this current time in the history of running 'the second running boom'. (The first running boom occurred in the 1970s and 1980s.)

Indeed, not since the first running boom has the world seen such an increase in the numbers of people taking to running. During the original running boom, experts estimated that 25 million Americans took up some aspect of running. Yet many believe that the current running boom outstrips the halcyon days of the first running boom, with estimates of 200 million people worldwide having taken to running in the last five to ten years.

Running events continue to grow every year in participation, with new competitors resulting in record entry numbers of competitors. Sold-out events, race organisers' websites crashing due to masses of traffic, and a bevy of new and quirky events typify the current running event landscape.

The new events offered show it's not just the traditional road running races that are booming. You can now run with paint being splashed all over you (Colour Run) or in the dark with glow sticks (Glow Run), cover many kilometres in events such as the Tough Mudder and the Spartan Race challenges, or even run steps inside stadiums (Stadium Stomps). All the while, the off-road and trail-running world of events is also exploding with an uptake in competitors and new races all the time. There's now even a mountain-running world series known as Sky Running.

Meanwhile, tens of thousands of runners pound the pavement on any given weekend – not for an event or a competition but, rather, just run for fitness or recreation. These recreational runners constitute a huge part of the worldwide second running boom, and show that not everyone has an interest in running for competition – some people run purely for fitness and health.

The boom in Australia and around the world

People of all ages, shapes and sizes are taking to running as a means of getting in shape and having fun. Running has become fashionable, and being a runner is now considered cool. Gone are the days when running was deemed as being uncool or uncultured. Gone are the days, when among friends, you were deemed a bit obsessive and weird if you classified yourself as a runner.

In days gone by you were considered very strange if you paid money to compete in running events. Things are different now. Running has become a mainstream and widely accepted and revered method of exercising for fitness and promoting optimal physical health.

The running boom of the 1970s and 1980s initially started in the USA. American marathoner Frank Shorter's victory in the 1972 Munich Olympic Marathon was credited with inspiring the boom. Shorter's win made him the first American Olympic marathon winner since 1908. However, it was arguably not the victory itself that intrigued Americans but rather the memorable and dramatic fashion by which a German imposter (a student not even in the race) crossed the line ahead of Shorter that captured imaginations and drew attention to marathon running.

In addition to Shorter's victory, other factors also acted as a catalyst for the groundswell and momentum of the first running boom in the USA. These included the rise of American track stars like Steve Prefontaine and his acclaimed coach (and Nike co-founder) Bill Bowerman, the acceptance of women as athletes across all sports, the beginnings of athletic scholarships being available at college level for women, and a rise in media coverage and new events such as the Chicago and New York Marathons. And so running morphed from the obsession of a few runners to a nationwide fad in the US and an accepted form of exercise.

As well as the USA, the first running boom spread to other countries, including the UK, Australia, and New Zealand. In contrast to the first running boom, this current second running boom is worldwide – it has not been isolated to one nation or even just several. The second running boom has swept all corners of the earth, and its sweep appears to be continuing very strongly, even as it heads into its third decade.

In Australia, 8 per cent of people over the age of 15 years identify themselves as runners.[1] In raw numbers, that equates to 1.65 million Australians partaking in some level of running activity at least two to three times a week. Interestingly, the number of Australians running or jogging as a sport has almost doubled since 2005–06.[2]

In the USA, since the mid-1990s Running USA (a national not-for-profit organisation) has documented the sport of running's rapid growth (2). According to their 2013 'State of the Sport' report, every year for the past 20 years (with the exception of 2003) has seen record numbers of race finishers in US running events. The report outlines that 2013 saw 15.3 million finishers in running events in the US alone. This equates to a staggering 170 per cent increase in numbers from 20 years earlier, or an 80 per cent increase since the year 2000.[3]

Even among some of the world's most smog-laden cities the running boom is in full swing. When a 10-kilometre road race in Hong Kong recently opened its online registration, the website crashed after 15 minutes as 30,000 people tried to secure registration. Amazingly, once the website was resurrected, the race was full within four hours.[4]

In the far East running's popularity is booming in China. On average, three marathon races are held each month on the Chinese mainland. The 33rd running of the Beijing Marathon hosted in excess of 30,000 runners, with all race entries submitted within 13 hours of registration opening. Yet in 1981 when the event was first launched, fewer than 200 people participated. Meanwhile, in 2013, the Shanghai Marathon attracted a record crowd of 35,000 runners just two months after the 33rd Beijing Marathon was held. Amazingly, on the same day, the Environmental Monitoring Centre reported pollution levels as being more than 10 times the World Health Organization's threshold. Perhaps most telling of the running boom sweeping China is the fact that the Chinese Athletic Association held 12 official running events in 2012 and an astonishing 53 official events in 2014.[5]

Meanwhile in Europe, research reveals that approximately 36 per cent of 15- to 65-year-old Europeans are taking to the streets, parks, forests and treadmills for their running fix. This finding was outlined in the ASICS 'Reasons to Run' survey, released in 2009. The same survey also revealed that Europe had approximately 80 million runners, with a third of them starting in the year that the survey was conducted. Incredibly, 33 per cent of European women started running in the year of the survey.[6]

The major beneficiaries of this second worldwide running boom are the footwear and running apparel manufacturers. The total dollars spent on jogging and running shoes in the USA alone in 2012 was a staggering $3.04 billion. Compared to 1998's $1.47 billion expenditure, this represents a 51.6 per cent increase in shoe sales, or an extra 15.2 million shoes being purchased. Sales are expected in the USA to grow to $3.51 billion in the not too distant future.[7]

Trend drivers

The question being asked is what is driving the explosion of people taking to running during this second worldwide running boom. Shoe companies, clothing manufacturers, event organisers and industry publications are all researching the key drivers. This research is finding that there are not just one or two key drivers at play; rather, a series of drivers appear to be fuelling the running boom.

Statistics sourced from formal running event participation records have helped identify the following key drivers of the second running boom:

> *Women:* A record number of women are taking to
> running. In the US, female finishers now comprise
> 56 per cent of the total competitors at any event,
> compared to 42 per cent in 2000. In 2012, 8.6 million
> females finished a US running event, and this had
> increased to 10.8 million women by 2013.[8]

> *Half marathons:* In the US alone, 2012 saw a record
> increase of 15 per cent (1.86 million runners) for finishers
> of the half-marathon distance, with 60 per cent of
> these being female. So far in 2014 in the US, there have
> been 1.96 million finishers with a 61 per cent female
> participation.[9]

> *5-kilometre events for beginners:* In the US, 40 per cent
> of all event finishers in 2012, or 6.8 million runners,
> completed a 5-kilometre running event. By 2013 this
> number had grown to 8.3 million race finishers of

a 5-kilometre event, making this the most popular distance.[10]

> *Ultra marathon runs:* Ultra marathons are defined as any race greater than the marathon distance (42.2 kilometres). In the last four years, participation in this sport has grown as much as it did in the previous 27 years. In 1998 in the US, there were 15,500 ultra-marathon finishers; in 2011, there were 52,000 ultra-marathon finishers. Furthermore, female participation has increased from virtually nil in the late 1970s to nearly 20 per cent since 2004.[11]

> *New, cool and 'hip' running events:* These are increasingly being added to the running calendar and include what could be classified as non-traditional running events, such as colour, mud, stadium, off-road and obstacle-type events. In the US alone analysts estimate that 2 million people participated in these types of events in 2012, growing to 4 million by 2013.[12]

> *Increases in traditional road running events:* New events are being added all the time, including charity runs and women-only runs. In the US in 2012, a total of 26,370 running events were conducted – representing at that stage an all-time high for the number of US events.[13]

> *Decreases in the popularity and participation of swimming.* In Australia, ABS figures show fewer people are swimming, and this may have been one of the key drivers of the doubling of participation in jogging and running as a sport or recreation since 2005–06.

> *Technology:* Websites, blogs, YouTube, forums, apps, and
> social media have all made it easier than ever to connect
> with a like-minded community of people who share a
> passion for running. This community and the technology
> available provides valuable and often times inspiring
> information for runners. Pre-technology, such runners
> would have never been able to connect in such a way.

So why do people run?

In addition to the preceding key drivers of the second running
boom, it's also interesting to consider the reasons or 'motivations'
that fuel individual participation and also help explain why so
many individuals have taken to running.

In 2009, shoe manufacturing giant ASICS embarked on
a large-scale research project they titled 'Research to Run',
interviewing 3500 runners from seven European nations in
order to discover the 'why' behind respondents desire to run.
What they discovered was that when getting started, fitness
and weight loss were the two most important factors. But they
also found that as an individual's running participation went
on, the benefits and reasons for running shifted. The longer
they ran, the more the runners studied began to recognise that
benefits were shifting from the physical body to the mind, with
35 per cent of these respondents running for stress relief and
34 per cent for fun.[14]

In preparing to write this book, I conducted my own
research to discover why people choose to run. My online

survey was completed by over one hundred runners, and my findings revealed five main motivations for why people were choosing to throw on their joggers and run. In rank order the key motivations why people chose to run were reported as being (from highest to lowest scoring):

> fitness

> personal challenge

> training for an event

> recreation

> being a professional athlete.

Just as the ASICS study revealed, the number one reason people were running was found in my survey to be for physical fitness. However, in addition to the preceding five reasons unearthed by my research project, further factors motivate individuals to run.

While not researched, I also believe additional motivations to take up running may include:

> Running offers great fitness gains for a very low time cost.

> Running is inexpensive – it can be done anywhere and anytime. No gym membership fees and no fancy equipment are required. The only necessity (outside of clothes) is a decent pair of running shoes.

> Running is a recession-proof pursuit. According to Running USA researcher Ryan Lamppa, running 'gives you something to control – you can't control the stock market or the economy, but you can control your health'.

> Charity runs are appealing. People love supporting a good cause and what better way than getting fit at the same time.

> Running is easily accessible and time efficient. This is particularly appealing to two groups of people. The first group comprises the busy male CEO/worker/and often times father who has an interest in staying fit but has time constraints. The other group who find the ease of accessibility appealing is women. Running allows women an efficient workout while still allowing them to meet the demands of work and home life.

> Running has a social aspect. New clubs and running groups are forming at an exponential rate. The key driver here is not the time-pressured and solo male runner but rather women seeking camaraderie and community. In the 2013 USA National Runners Survey, 33 per cent of respondents said they would be more likely to run if they had a companion or some company to do it with.

> Running is trendy. Today's event organisers pay very special attention to making each participant's experience as memorable as possible. It's appealing to complete an event and win the kudos of your friends, co-workers and family at the finish line. Finishers at events today can claim everything from a medal, finish photo to a personalised race finish video and photo.

The benefits, myths, and facts

It is well accepted that running produces many positive effects on the body. Scientific research has proven that exercise such as running is associated with a wide array of health benefits. These benefits include:

> lower risk of cardiovascular disease

> lower risk of stroke

> lower risk of high blood pressure

> lowered risk of osteoporosis

> lower risk of type 2 diabetes

> lower risk of colon and breast cancer

> reduced risk of clinical depression

> better management of body weight and body mass index

> better cognitive function.

In fact, researchers have even discovered that running may be the 'magic pill' of good health, and the 'fountain of youth' we would all seek.

A 2014 study found that, compared with non-runners, runners have an incredible 45 to 50 per cent lessened chance of dying from cardiovascular disease. Researchers also found that runners had a three year increase in life expectancy when compared to non-runners! What makes this study and its results so remarkable is that the study included an enormous 55,137 subjects with 24 per cent (13,233) of the subjects being runners.[15] One of the other key findings of this study was that running for even a short time and at slow speeds was enough to result in the markedly reduced risk of dying from cardiovascular disease.

Interestingly, this study paralleled the findings of a study published six years earlier. Researchers at Stanford University looked at 538 runners and 423 healthy non-runners who were all greater than 50 years of age. After 19 years, only 15 per cent of the runners had died, yet 34 per cent of the non-runners had died. At a follow-up 21 years later, the difference in mortality rates was even more pronounced. This same paper also showed that running reduces the incidence of disability later in life, yielding a higher quality of life in addition to a longer life.[16]

Science has even dismissed the veracity of the 'running will wear out your knees' argument that many non-runners cite as a good reason to not run. Researchers at Stanford University investigated the differences in the progression of knee osteoarthritis in middle to older aged runners over two decades. In the analysis, long distance running was not associated with either accelerated incidence or severity of knee osteoarthritis.[17] Another study showed that former competitive runners did not have higher rates of arthritis in their hips, knees or ankles when compared to non-runners.[18]

With so many health benefits derived from exercise, more runners in the world would surely mean more healthy bodies in the world. The flow-on effect from healthier individuals would be healthier families, communities and, ultimately, a healthier global population. There would appear to be little or no downside to more people participating in running as a sport, for fitness or as a recreational pursuit.

A runner will, however, encounter one problem, the problem of injury.

Although running has not been shown to cause greater rates of knee osteoarthritis or arthritis, running injuries are unfortunately not infrequent. The exact incidence of running injuries is not known in terms of a single number or statistic. Rather, the incidence of running-related injuries among runners varies in the scientific literature.

One review examined 1,137 scientific titles and abstracts and cut this initial list down to 17 articles that were of good quality in order to establish the incidence of running-related injury. The running injury incidence rate was reported to vary from 19.4 to 79.3 per cent.[19] Another study reported the incidence rate of running-related injury to be as high as 92.4 per cent.[20]

An additional review found that for the average recreational runner who is steadily training and who participates semi-regularly in a long distance event, the overall yearly incidence rate for a running injury is between 37 and 56 per cent. This same paper also expressed the injury incidence rate as a number relative to 1,000 running hours, and found that incidence was between 2.5 to 12.1 injuries per 1,000 hours of running. The paper also reported a high recurrence rate of running injuries that ranged from 20 to 70 per cent.[21]

One retrospective study of 2,886 runners reported an overall injury rate of 46 per cent.[22] Meanwhile reports reveal that injury incidence rates for runners training for the marathon can be as high as 90 per cent.[23]

One study found that out of 1,049 runners competing in fun runs held in Brazil, 22 per cent of them reported an injury before a race.[24] That is equivalent to almost one-quarter of the field standing on the start line ready to compete in the fun run injured.

The problem with being injured is that the health benefits that running produces are not being experienced. One of the preceding studies concluded that running injuries led to a reduction of training or training cessation in about 30 to 90 per cent of all injuries.[25] So the majority of injured runners will need to stop their running due to their injury.

Whichever statistic you look at, none are overly promising. They all point toward the fact that the large bulk of runners (well over half) will end up injured in some way every year. It's certainly not exciting for the beginner runner looking to make a start. It's equally unpalatable to the competitive runner seeking to consistently train for an upcoming event. And it's a very serious threat to the health of the over-stressed male executive high performer who was just about to start a running training program after being informed he has high blood pressure and cholesterol.

Simple arithmetic tells us that as the participation of runners increases worldwide as part of the global running boom so too will the numbers of injured runners. The correlation between participation and injuries certainly appears to be holding true in the consulting room, where I have observed a spike in the last several years of running-related injuries.

This is never more evident than when my home city of the Gold Coast hosts its annual marathon weekend, which includes a variety of runs – from a 5-kilometre race to the full distance marathon. In the lead up to this event my diary is normally oversubscribed with injured runners, ranging from first timers to the over-zealous and well-seasoned runner who is pushing for a personal best performance.

Running into injury – key points

Here are the main points to take away from this chapter:

> The world is experiencing what trend analysts refer to as the 'second running boom'. More people are now running than at any stage in history!

> Numerous key drivers are behind the worldwide running boom, including an increase in the numbers of women running, the addition of countless new road and novel running events, the appeal of the half-marathon distance as a fitness challenge, and technology that is making information readily available to runners of all levels.

> Runners have their own individual reasons for choosing to run. Beginners tend to start running for fitness and weight loss. As they continue, the mental rewards of running become the key reason for continuing to run.

> The incidence of running injuries is high among runners. One study reported the incidence rate to be as high as 92.4 per cent. A large bulk of runners will end up injured in any given year.

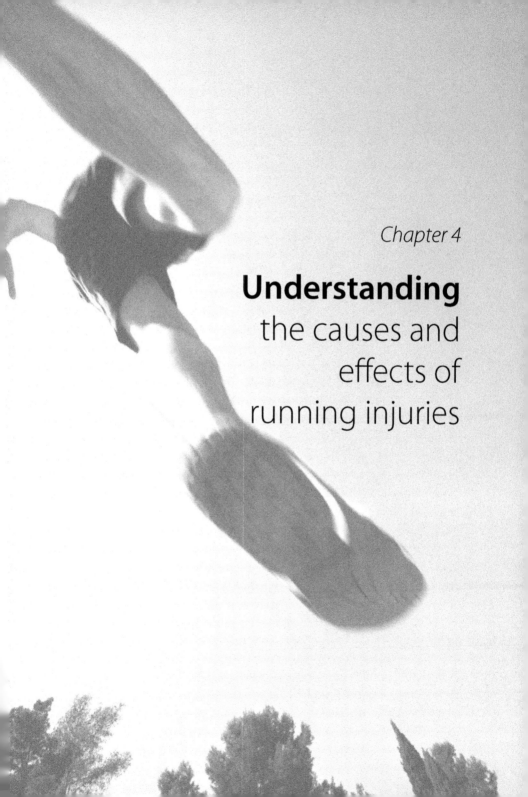

Chapter 4

Understanding
the causes and
effects of
running injuries

The most common running injuries

With so many runners being injured in any given year of running, it's important that we look at what the commonly incurred injuries are. As with any sport, running involves sports-specific injuries that are most commonly experienced by runners.

The bulk – 50 to 75 per cent of injuries sustained by runners – are what we term 'overuse' or 'repetitive strain' injuries.[1] Overuse injuries are injuries that develop due to the repetitive loading and repetitive movements of a particular sport. These injuries build up over a period of time in response to the accumulation of micro trauma on the body's tissues. In the case of running, this cumulative loading is the result of the repetitive movements of running.

An example of an overuse injury for a runner is the onset of 'shin splints'. Over the course of months, as the shin bones are subjected to ever-increasing repetitive loads, the pain in the runner's shins gets progressively worse. Eventually, continued running will cause the runner to stop when the shins become so sore that running without pain is no longer possible.

While overuse injuries rank among the most common running injuries, many runners also experience what are termed 'acute' injuries. Acute injuries are the result of a one-off high force or macro trauma to the body's tissues. An example is the runner who sustains a calf muscle strain while out running. There is no 'build up', just a simple step and then 'bang' – pain as the muscle tissue is disrupted by a tear.

Given that the purpose of this book is to assist runners to avoid the onset of injury, I will provide a brief overview of the most commonly experienced running inures. This section is by no means intended to be a comprehensive injury reference guide.

Before we delve into the five step method of preventing running injuries, it is important that we have an appreciation of what the most commonly experienced running injuries are. These injuries are outlined in the following sections.

Knee pain or 'runner's knee'

Technically this is known as 'patello-femoral pain'. This occurs when irritation and subsequent pain are produced from disturbed movements between the knee cap (patella) and the underlying groove in the bone that the knee cap rests on top of (the femur). According to a runnersworld.com poll of 4,500 respondents, about 40 per cent of runners experience knee pain, and 13 per cent suffered knee pain inside a year.[2] One study reported that the most common site of running related injury was the knee with an incidence rate of 7.2 to 50 per cent.[3]

Chief causes and signs to look for are as follows:

> *Chief causes:* tight muscle surrounding the knee (quadriceps, hamstrings, calves), restricted fascia around the patella, weakness of the hip muscles, training loads suddenly increased, inappropriate footwear, excess body weight, and poor running technique.

> *Signs to look for:* pain behind the knee cap that is made worse with running, prolonged periods of sitting, pain with going up and down stairs (down is often worse), and catching pain getting in and out of a car or from a low height.

Plantar fasciitis

It should be no surprise that one of the most frequently injured body areas are runners' feet, and indeed experts estimate that 15 per cent of all running injuries strike the feet.[4] Plantar fascia pain is by far the most common cause of foot pain in runners, estimated to account for 8 per cent of all running-related foot injuries,[5] with an incidence rate ranging from 4.5 to 10 per cent.[6]

Similar to the tendon changes that affect the Achilles tendon, the plantar fascia itself does not tend to get inflamed, despite what the Latin suffix 'itis' in plantar fasciitis denotes (in Latin, 'itis' means 'inflammation of'). Rather the fascia undergoes a gradual decline in its strength and tissue quality, as the runner experiences a proportionate and gradual increase in the pain on the sole of their foot.

Here are the chief causes and signs to look for:

> *Chief causes:* tight muscle surrounding the foot (calves, tibialis anterior), restricted fascia around the heel, weakness of the hip muscles, training loads suddenly increased, inappropriate footwear, flat feet or dropped arches, excess body weight, and poor running technique.

> *Signs to look for:* pain on the sole of the foot close to the heel bone, pain that is made worse with running, pain with getting out of bed in the morning, or 'start up' pain after prolonged periods of sitting as the first steps are taken.

ITB (ilio-tibial band) friction syndrome

This condition makes up 12 per cent of all running-related overuse injuries.[7] Pain typically develops on the outside of the thigh (femur) just above and to the outside of the knee joint. When the knee straightens and bends through the running cycle, the ilio-tibial band can more or less 'rub' on the outside of the thigh bone and create what can either be dull or, at its worst, very sharp pain.

Chief causes and signs to look for are as follows:

> *Chief causes:* tight muscle surrounding the knee (quadriceps, hamstrings, calves), restricted fascia around the outside of the patella, weakness of the hip muscles, training loads suddenly increased, inappropriate footwear, flat feet or dropped arches, excess body weight, and poor running technique.

> *Signs to look for:* pain on the outside of the knee that is made worse with running, or pain with deep squatting type movements. The pain can either be dull or at times very sharp. Many runners often mistake this pain as being an intrinsic knee joint injury (for example a meniscus tear) due to the high level pain it can at times produce.

'Shin splints'

Pain in the shin bone (tibia) has been reported to make up 12 to 18 per cent of all running injuries,[8] with female runners experiencing shin pain more than male runners. Technically 'shin splints' is not a diagnosis but rather an umbrella term that includes a variety of pathologies that can strike the region of the shin bone (tibia).

These pathologies can include problems with nearby tendons, exertional pains of the connective tissue near the shin, and a gamut of tibia-related pains. The medical term for shin splints is 'medial tibial stress syndrome' (MTSS). However, most people refer to this condition simply as 'shin splints'. In practice, I tend to refer to MTSS as shin splints or 'shin pain' due to the familiarity of these terms among runners.

Many runners incorrectly believe that they have shin splints when they experience pain at the front and outside of their shin bone. Normally this is not shin splints but rather muscle and fascia tightness of the tibialis anterior muscle. The tibialis anterior muscles can be prone to becoming excessively tight when exercise is commenced. Pain to the front and outside of the shin can result from reduced or restricted blood flow to the tibialis anterior muscle. Medically we term this pain 'compartment syndrome', and its cause is distinctly different to a true case of shin splints.

Authentic shin splints develop in the bottom third of the shin bone. It is at this point that the shin bone has the smallest cross-sectional area, and so is the most vulnerable to repetitive loading and subsequent injury at this point.

Shin splints is a continuum condition, whereby the shin bone will progress from being normally loaded, to slightly overloaded, to very overloaded, to eventually incurring fracture. During the 'overloading' stages the bone becomes painful as the outside of the bone (the cortex) develops tiny microscopic fracture lines. At a cellular level, when pain is experienced the bone's repair mechanisms are being outstripped by the bone being damaged and broken down.

The very end stage of shin splints is a tibial stress fracture. At this point the bone fails and fractures due to being repeatedly overloaded beyond its tolerance or 'failure point' through continued stress and loading associated with running.

Here are the chief causes and signs to look out for with shin splints:

> *Chief causes:* tight calf muscles, weakness in the calf muscles, training loads suddenly increased, addition of hills and hard surfaces to a training program, inappropriate footwear, flat feet or dropped arches, excess body weight, and poor running technique.

> *Signs to look for:* pain in the bottom one third of the shin bone. The pain is felt on the inside border of the shin. Initially, the shin will be sore to touch after running. As the shin bone continues to be overloaded, the pain usually progresses to being present at the start of a run. Eventually if treatment and rest are not sought and adhered to, the shin bone will be sore before, during and after running. When a stress fracture occurs, the runner will have difficulty hopping on a single leg two to three times because the pain will be too great.

Hamstring injuries

The hamstrings are big and powerful muscles – spanning from the bottom muscles (the gluts) and extending down below the line of the knee. The hamstrings are used extensively when running to pull the thigh backwards during the propulsion phase of the running gait, and to also slow down the rate at which the knees straighten just before impact with the ground. According to the Runners World poll, 7 per cent of runners polled reported having hamstring 'troubles' inside the year of polling.[9]

The two most common hamstring problems for runners are acute muscle tears and hamstring tendon problems. The three hamstring muscles insert via a common tendon onto the sitting bone, and this common tendon insertion point can become a site of pain due to a range of conditions that collectively represent hamstring tendon injuries. These conditions can include tendonopathies and tendonosis (change in the tendon's composition), tears, or even enthesopathies (changes in the tendon to bone interface).

Acute muscle tears are typically experienced in the outside or lateral hamstring, known as the biceps femoris muscle. As with calf muscle tears (see the section 'Calf injuries' later in this chapter for more information), the tear typically occurs in the middle of the muscle belly or at the point where the hamstring muscle joins into its tendon. These tears are felt as an acute and sudden onset of pain. Alternately, hamstring tendon injuries typically take time to develop and are experienced just under the sitting bone. In these cases, the tendon begins to degenerate, which subsequently produces pain.

55

Muscle strains can be divided into three well-recognised categories, ranging from grade 1 to grade 3 tears. Grade 3 tears are medically referred to as being 'full thickness' tears. This means that a tear has gone vertically 'through' the muscle belly. (This is not to be confused with muscle 'ruptures', which is where a muscle pulls completely away from a bone at the point of the muscle's tendon insertion.) Grade 1 and 2 muscle tears indicate partial tearing of the muscle. These tears can occur either where the muscle inserts into the tendon (the myo-tendinous junction), or in the muscle belly itself.

Chief causes and signs to look for with hamstring injuries include the following:

> *Chief causes:* tight quadriceps and hamstring muscles, weakness of the hip stability muscles (which overloads the hamstring muscles), training loads suddenly increased, addition of hills and hard surfaces to a training program, stiff lower back structures (for example joints), inappropriate footwear, flat feet or dropped arches, excess body weight, and poor running technique.

> *Signs to look for:* acute hamstring tears will typically be felt in the outside hamstring region (biceps femoris) with a sudden movement. The muscles are most susceptible to tears when the hamstring is being used to slow down the runner's rate of landing at the time of ground impact. Minor strains will allow the runner to run on (grade 1), whereas grade 2 or 3 strains will typically require the runner to stop running and seek help.

Hamstring tendon pain is made worse with running and activity. As the condition worsens, pain may be experienced with pressure from sitting (for example, when driving a car), and with movements such as going from sitting to standing.

Achilles tendon injuries

Despite the fact that the Achilles tendon is the strongest tendon in the human body, it indeed can be the 'Achilles heel' for many runners, with Achilles tendon problems making up 11 per cent of all running injuries.[10] Almost all of the force generated as your toes push off when running is transmitted through the Achilles tendon. At speed this can be up to three times your body weight. This is why many runners will succumb to Achilles tendon injuries.

A variety of injuries can affect the Achilles tendon, with the most common being tendonopathy of the Achilles tendon, which can be mid-portion or insertional. Another injury is acute tendon tears, which can range from a partial thickness tear to a full thickness tear of the tendon.

With ongoing research, the medical world's understanding of tendon behaviour has markedly changed over the last several years. For the two decades before this, the diagnosis of 'Achilles tendinitis' was all too prevalent, but therapists now rarely provide such a diagnosis. The affected tendons previously thought to be inflamed were found to not have any inflammatory component, and so the Latin suffix 'itis' (which means 'inflammation of') has been dropped. Tendinitis is now referred to as tendonopathy, which more accurately reflects the adverse changes that progressively occur inside the tendon itself.

With tendonopathy, a continuum of tendon 'breakdown' exists. Initially, the tendon loses its integrity and strength as it is infiltrated at a cellular level with painful proteins. The tendon will progress from initially being sore and 'reactive', to a phase known as 'dysrepair'. Eventually, the final stage of 'degeneration' of the tendon results.

The Achilles tendon can be affected at the point where the tendon inserts into the heel bone (insertional tendonopathy) or in the middle of the Achilles tendon approximately 2 to 7 centimetres above the heel bone (mid-portion tendonopathy). About two-thirds of tendon problems occur at the mid-portion of the Achilles, with the other one-third affecting the Achilles tendon at the site of insertion into the heel bone. Management of these two sites of tendon problems varies.

With insertional tendon pain the clinician needs to guide the runner through minimising the compression of the tendon. With mid-portion tendon pain the clinician needs to mainly decrease tensile tendon loading patterns.

The causes and signs of Achilles tendon problems are as follows:

> *Chief causes:* tight calf muscles, weakness in the calf muscles, training loads suddenly increased, sudden addition of hill running, inappropriate footwear, flat feet or dropped arches, excess body weight, poor running technique, and stiff mid-foot joints.

> *Signs to look for:* Achilles tendon tears will be acutely felt in a similar fashion to calf tears. The chief difference

between a calf muscle tear and an Achilles tendon tear will be that the pain for an Achilles tear will be felt much lower towards the heel bone.

Tendonopathy pain will progressively worsen with time. Initially the tendon will feel 'stiff' when getting out of bed or getting up to walk after a period of prolonged sitting. The tendon will then become tender to touch, and eventually the tendon will be sore before, during, and after running.

Calf injuries

Unfortunately, most runners at some stage in their running life will experience a calf strain or 'tear'. The calf is made up of two large muscles – the gastrocnemius and soleus. Gastrocnemius is the muscle closer to the skin and is more vulnerable to injury. The soleous sits underneath the calf with injuries to the soleous occurring far less commonly.

Researchers do not routinely report calf injury incidence rates in isolation, but rather often combine calf injuries with Achilles injuries. One study reported that the injury incidence rate of Achilles and calf injuries among 2002 running injuries was 6.4 per cent.[11]

Typically calf strains occur quickly and create instant pain and discomfort. The strains (or tears) are categorised from grade 1 to grade 3 (refer to the section 'Hamstring injuries' for information on this grading system).

The chief causes and signs to look out for are as follows:

> *Chief causes:* tight calf muscles, weakness in the calf muscles, training loads suddenly increased, inappropriate

footwear, flat feet or dropped arches, excess body weight, and poor running technique.

> *Signs to look for:* quick onset of pain typically felt in either the outside, inside, or middle of the calf. The pain will be worse with physical activity. Running may not be possible or at best very painful. The injured runner may walk with a limp and the foot turned outwards to decrease pain with walking.

Note that calf pain can also come from non-traumatic causes such as generalised tightness or soreness. This is normally the result of doing too much running or by having weak claves.

Will the five steps safeguard me from injury?

While the injuries covered in the preceding sections all represent potential problems for runners, the good news is that by implementing my five step method of running pain and injury free outlined in this book, you will markedly reduce your likelihood of sustaining an injury. Of course, I would like to tell you that after reading this book you will never again experience a running-related injury. However, this is entirely dependent on your diligence with applying each of the five steps.

As you read the book, I want you to think of the five steps as your 'insurance policy' – one that will help protect you from running injuries. As with any insurance policy, it will be void and ineffective unless it is current and renewed. In other words, remaining injury free requires your ongoing and constant application of the five steps I outline in this book.

If you do sustain a running-related injury I suggest you engage the help of a medical practitioner such a physiotherapist. Don't try to be a 'home treatment hero'. The problem with home and self-care treatments is that, at best, you can only address the symptoms of your injury. The underlying causative factors that produced the injury will typically remain unaddressed. The result is a much heightened risk of re-injury.

Understanding injury causation

Very rarely is the onset of a running-related injury caused by a single factor. However, understandably, the notion of there being a single contributing or causative factor of injury onset is highly palatable to most injured runners. If just one causative factor existed, then just this sole factor would need to be addressed in order to 'fix' the injury. Sadly, as convenient as a sole contributory factor would be, the notion of a single causative injury factor tends to be wishful thinking on the behalf of most injured runners.

If injury onset was caused by only one contributory factor, injury rehabilitation would become quite straightforward. It would involve less heartache for both the injured runner and the treating therapist. However, the reality of any running-related injury is that a combination of contributing or causative factors will have led to the development of a given injury.

A skilled practitioner is able to thoroughly assess the injured runner and identify the unique combination of contributing factors that led to the development of the injury. The skilled practitioner is then able to articulate these causative injury factors to the injured runner before addressing each of the contributing factors with appropriate rehabilitation strategies.

When all of the contributing factors have been addressed, a full solution to the injury will have been achieved. In other words, if all contributory factors have been addressed the therapist will have helped the injured runner safeguard themselves against ongoing problems or injury recurrence – in effect, the runner at this point has taken out 'injury insurance'.

In my practice I show a diagram similar to the one opposite to my clients in order to help them understand the concept of an injury causation due to a combination of contributory factors. I will often add an approximate percentage of contribution for each factor in the overall causation of the injury. Each of the different contributing factors is represented by different sized boxes in the diagram, with the bigger boxes representing greater injury causation.

Contributing factors that could be listed in an injury causation diagram include the following:

> age-related degeneration (for example osteoarthritis)

> anatomical abnormalities (for example 'bowed legs')

> biomechanics

> congenital conditions (for example perthes or hip dysplasia)

> core stability

> foot type

> gait (walking style)

> footwear (for example the wearing of high heels or inappropriate running shoes)

> joint hyper/hypomobility

> occupation

> pelvic control

> running technique

> previous injury

> tight muscles surrounding a joint or body area

> training errors

> trauma to the body.

Injury causation diagram

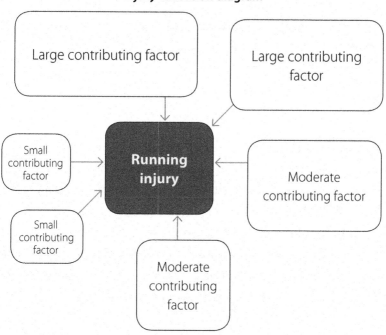

Typically most running-related injuries will have two to three major contributing factors. Collectively, these factors may represent 60 to 80 per cent of the contribution towards the injury onset.

For example, when reviewing the seven most common running injuries listed previously in this chapter, you may notice that muscle tightness, weakness of the hips, and sudden changes in training load are listed as chief causes for all of the seven injuries. A well-constructed injury rehabilitation program will aim to immediately address these contributing factors. By quickly addressing the major contributing factors, the injured runner will experience pain reduction and functional improvements in the quickest manner possible.

The other smaller contributing factors can then be addressed over a longer period of time in order to ensure a full injury solution is achieved, and to also minimise the risk of further aggravation or re-injury.

The real problem with being injured

When a running injury strikes the problem normally extends well beyond the pain of the physical injury sustained. The pain that is experienced as result of the injury is normally just one element of what the injured runner will be experiencing.

For injured runners the problem is usually not so much the sore foot, sore knee, sore shin, or irritated hamstring. Most runners are quite adept at managing the physical side of their pain, and injured runners can normally make themselves at least 'comfortable' with their pain until they get to see a physiotherapist or health care provider.

However, if you 'scratch below the surface' and probe an injured runner about their mood, attitude, and general sense of wellbeing, the vast majority of injured runners will be wrestling with some resultant emotional and psychological challenges. The degree of their 'head battles' can be wide ranging in terms of emotion and impact.

The scale of emotional unrest will vary depending on how important running is in the life of the runner. For example, the recreational runner who cannot exercise because of injury may feel anxious and 'glum', or a bit 'flat or down'. Meanwhile, the more competitive or seasoned runner whose injury threatens a major upcoming event into which hours of training have been devoted may experience a case of mild to advanced clinical depression. These are examples only and the recreational runner may also experience a depressed mood or even clinical depression if they are unable to run for a protracted period of time. My clinical observations and in practice dialogue with injured runners verify the emotional and mental effects of being injured.

In my research for this book, the greatest problems injured runners reported they experienced were not related to the physical pain of their previous or current injuries. Rather, the psychological aspects of the injury were what negatively impacted the injured runner the most.

The following were given as the main problems injured runners experienced:

> frustration with the injury that won't go away

> not knowing what to do (confusion)

> not knowing who to turn to for help (confusion)

> losing fitness while not training

> gaining weight while not training

> fear of the injury returning once training is resumed

> loss of confidence in one's physical wellness/abilities

> feeling 'torn' between resting and training.

Debunking the injury myth

In clinical practice I have spent thousands of hours working with injured runners. One interesting yet sad realisation I have come to is that almost every runner believes that they will become injured at some stage. They believe that if they run for long enough and far enough, it will be inevitable that an injury will develop at some stage.

They erroneously accept injury as being normal, believing that injury is to running as the night and day are to the earth – one will inevitably follow the other. The majority of runners, if not all runners, believe that developing injuries is a normal part of the running experience. Most runners do not truly believe that it is possible to run pain and injury free over a sustained period of time.

As a physio dedicated to rehabilitating runners, this unfounded belief frustrates me enormously. The fact that so many runners run with an expectation and anticipation of getting injured is I believe unfounded and self-limiting. Their misguided thinking is in effect short-changing their running experience. My frustration is borne of the fact that I know that there is a better way.

In my practice, I teach runners that *it is* actually possible to run pain and injury free. An ancient proverb says that hope deferred makes the heart grow sick. I know that unless I restore hope and confidence for the injured runner, they will continue to run with the anticipation that an injury is coming 'their way' at some stage, and in essence, their deferred hope will 'make them sick'.

I spend a lot of energy educating injured runners that they can and, in fact, should expect to run pain and injury free. I challenge their thinking about the high incidence of running injuries, and their default acceptance that this will be their experience too. I coach them through their rehabilitation towards injury recovery by guiding them through the five steps of pain and injury free running enclosed in this book.

At some point in their recovery the injured runner's 'lights go on'. This light bulb moment happens when they realise that it is possible to not get injured if the right training and body conditions are adhered to.

My five step method has worked for thousands of runners that I have treated throughout my professional life. It is the same method that I too have implemented into my very own running which has seen me run pain and injury free like I never believed to be possible.

You don't have to believe the generationally espoused misunderstanding that running will inevitably result in injury. Despite the sombre injury statistics included in this chapter, reading this book will equip you to get your shoes on and get running, and to do so in a way that truly minimises and prevents injury onset. Reading this book will unlock your potential to enjoy injury- and pain-free running. This book will help you smash the false belief that injury is an inevitable part of a runner's life. You are about to discover that it is possible to run pain and injury free!

So, here we go! After checking out the key points for this chapter, you can lean in and start with step one.

Understanding the causes and effects of injury – key points

Here are the main points to take away from this chapter:

> Running injuries are caused by more than one sole contributory factor; instead a combination of contributory factors will be behind the majority of running-related injuries.

> Identifying and addressing all of the contributory factors of an injury is the key to true and effective rehabilitation. All factors (small and large) must be addressed for complete rehabilitation to be achieved.

> The greatest challenge for runners when they experience injury is typically not the physical pain experienced. Rather, the mental or psychological impact that the injury has on the injured runner's life

Understanding the causes and effects of injury – key points (continued)

is often the greater problem that the injured runner experiences.

> Despite the high injury incidence rates, believing that sustaining injury is inevitable for runners is erroneous. There is a better way of thinking. The five step method in this book will reveal the steps required to run with confidence and an expectation of pain- and injury-free running.

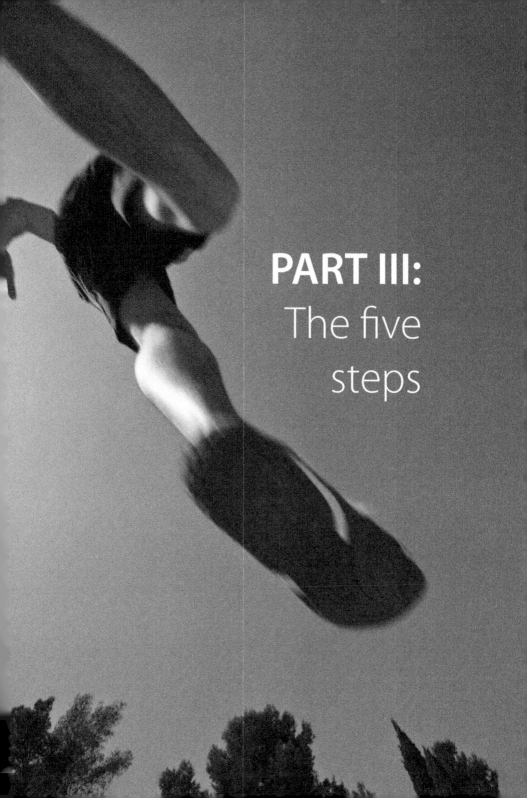

PART III:
The five
steps

Chapter 5

STEP 1: Discover your running body

Step 1: Discover your running body

Step 2: Run with great technique

Step 3: Navigate the footwear maze

Step 4: The importance of hip stability

Step 5: The power of rest

Point A and Point B

All journeys start with a single step. The journey towards running pain and injury free is no different. The first step on this journey is to get to know your 'running body'. This foundational step is an imperative launch pad – it's what makes the four steps that follow possible.

As with any successful 'change program', having a firm understanding and awareness of your starting position before an intervention commences is crucial. In this case, the five steps are the intervention that will take you on a journey from your starting position (Point A) to your destination (Point B).

Every successful journey to somewhere worthwhile has a known starting point – simply the point where you leave from. Your starting position (your Point A) may be that you're:

> currently injured and looking for solutions to help get you back to running pain free

> not currently injured but your efforts to train have been previously hampered by recurring and consistent injuries

> not injured and never have been (unlikely) and you wish to remain that way.

Whatever your Point A happens to be you have picked up this book because you don't want to stay stuck at Point A. You want to get to your Point B. Because you're reading this book, I assume that your Point B is (as the book's title states) to run pain and injury free and as a result faster.

In order to successfully journey from point A to point B, you need to benchmark your starting position. The better you understand and record your starting position, the more likely you are to arrive at your Point B, pain- and injury-free running.

Understanding your body's genetic endowment with respect to your mobility status, and your body's strengths and potential weaknesses will begin to set you on a trajectory to enjoy pain- and injury-free running.

Benchmarking your starting position

The benefits of benchmarking your starting position are many. The motivation gained through comparing progress achieved with a set starting position applies to any effective health change program – for example, formal psychological counselling programs, weight loss programs, or even yoga programs.

With my five steps to pain- and injury-free running, benchmarking your Point A will primarily provide you with the ability to effectively monitor changes that result from the five steps. Your monitored progress will then provide motivation to 'keep going' when results may slow or seem non-existent for a period of time. Without knowing where you started, it's very difficult if not impossible to be motivated or enthused by any progress, or maintain motivation during any lack of progress that occurs.

This initial benchmarking will serve as the 'fuel' to implement your learnings from all five steps and to arrive at your Point B.

Another benefit of benchmarking your starting position is that it allows you to evaluate your progress against your goals. It has been said that experience is not a useful teacher, but rather evaluated experience is the only useful teacher. Without a benchmarked Point A, future efforts to better understand what works for you and what doesn't in terms of keeping you injury free will not be as easily identifiable.

Recognising your genetic gifts – your physical attributes

Genetics is a fascinating science. Its wonders are unending, and it largely remains one of life's great mysteries. The field of genetics challenges the minds of all who try to unlock its mysteries – the mysteries of genetic trait endowment.

For some, genetics is a great enabler of physical performance. A great gift of physical potential or prowess is passed on from their parents or even their grandparents – it wasn't earned in any way, but it was merely inherited. A product of good fortune, luck or favour – whatever term you wish to use. Look at any modern-day sporting great and you will likely observe the magic mix of a superior athletic gene pool and the athlete's commitment and discipline to maximise their genetic potential.

In the world of distance running, some runners are genetically gifted with great aerobic capacities or 'engines'. They have greater than normal heart and lung function, which allows them utilise more oxygen per kilogram of body weight each minute of running. In the word of science this measure of heart and lung function is known as 'VO2max' (pronounced 'vee oh-two max'). VO2max is measured as a number, and the higher the number the better the aerobic engine the athlete has. The athlete cannot do anything to 'earn' a high VO2max. It is a genetically determined number that the athlete is born with.

Inheriting a high VO2max score is a genetic gift that makes conquering endurance running events and posting magnificent times possible. This might be in the form of a world-class marathon time or perhaps a world-class 10-kilometre or 5-kilometre time. At the time of writing, the world marathon record is 2:02:57, set by Dennis Kimetto of Kenya at the 2014 Berlin Marathon. To put that in perspective that is equivalent to running in excess of 20 kilometres per hour for more than 2 hours!

Experts have long known that people from African nations such as Kenya and Ethiopia have genetic distance-running prowess. Pick any long-distance race and in most, up to 80 per cent of winners since the late 1980s have been from Kenya. For example since 1988, 20 of the 25 first-place men in the world's longest running marathon – the Boston Marathon – have been from Kenya.

In contrast, over shorter sprinting distances a runner may inherit sprinting genes that offer them the potential for world-class speed. As with the African nations' dominance and genetic prowess in distance running, experts have identified that Jamaican people carry a gene that makes them superior sprinters. When we saw Usain Bolt hit a top speed of 42 kilometres per hour to win the London Olympic Games 100-metre final in an Olympic record time of 8.63 seconds (just 0.05 seconds shy of his 2009 world record time of 8.58 seconds) we were witnessing the wonders of genetics at work.

Of course, it wasn't only Usain's genetic prowess that allowed him to claim the title of history's fastest man. In addition to making use of his genetic gifts, he too has had to discover his running body. With this knowledge he has then trained hard, attempted to remain injury free, and set about maximising his genetic potential. For any runner, remaining injury free is a key to unlocking running potential.

The world-class distance runners that receive our rightful admiration inherit physical attributes that make such running and performances possible. If you were an aspiring world-class elite distance runner, your 'genetic wish list' might include a body that:

> is very lean and light

> has less mass for any respective height

> has a greater leg length to torso length ratio

> has straight legs with little or no bowing of the legs

> has hips that are aligned in a 'neutral' position

> has a small and light pelvis

> has very small ankles and shins to allow for better heat dissipation and lower energy costs to move the limbs

> has a tendency to more stability (rather than excessive mobility) around the joints

> has a high V02max aerobic capacity

> a high natural 'haematocrit' (red blood cell density measure).

Facing up to your genetics – your physical attributes

After reading the preceding section, you may feel, as an aspiring runner, like genetics has not been kind to you. Perhaps you have inherited physical attributes that don't match those on the world-class runner list. In fact, your physical attributes may be the exact opposite of the entire elite runner's physical attributes list.

Whether you are aiming to run for mere recreation and fitness, or whether you harbour competition goals, you may feel like you are 'cursed' genetically.

Maybe you have a longer torso to leg length ratio, aren't naturally a light frame, or have bowed legs. If this describes you, the key message is don't despair. Certainly do not become discouraged. Only a very small percentage of the world's population are gifted elite-level distance runners. Yet the world is full of runners and, as you read in chapter 1, the global running community is exploding. Even though it is the genetically gifted who tend to run the fastest, there are more runners worldwide enjoying running than just the thin ranks of the elite.

The central message and purpose in writing this book is to empower people (like you) to know that you can run pain and injury free. Running pain and injury free is for everybody, irrespective of your physical genetic gifts or lack thereof. Just because your physical attributes vary from the world's elite runners physical checklist doesn't mean you shouldn't start or persist with your running. You absolutely should and nothing should deter you.

As a junior runner I spent many hours at a physio practice receiving treatment for my array of running injuries. For the first time in my young life (and well before I entered the physiotherapy profession) I began to understand my inherited physical traits and how they affected my performance. I'd inherited my father's bowed legs (or in physio speak 'genu varum'), 'tibial torsion' (rotated shin bones), and relatively flat feet.

On paper and biomechanically, this genetic 'recipe' represented a greater inclination towards the development of running injuries. Unfortunately for me as a junior triathlete and runner, this proved true. Yet, despite my less than ideal genetic traits, in the long run I have not been held back in my ability to run fast and pain free.

I now enjoy running as much as I like with no regular running-related injuries. Many health practitioners might look at the combination of traits of my inherited leg shape and declare it not likely that I would be able to run injury free. Yet, for the last six years I have been running almost daily and consistently continue to set personal best times across distances of 5 kilometres to full marathons.

In addition to my own experience with not letting genetic disadvantages cruel my desire to enjoy running, I have observed thousands of case studies in my physio practice. I have seen countless injured runners, with all sorts of body shapes, successfully return to enjoying pain- and injury-free running by applying my five step methodology.

So don't despair if your gene pool appears to have been unkind or less favourable than you would have liked. Despite your genetic physical attributes, you can look forward to running pain and injury free.

Body awareness: your genetic mobility status

In addition to your body's inherited physical attributes, you also inherit your overall body 'mobility status'. Your mobility status is basically how much or how little movement you 'naturally' have around your joints. Mobility status is a key genetic trait that you need to understand in order to get the most of your running body.

Some people inherit either one of two ends of a mobility spectrum. That is, they are either very mobile or flexible (hypermobile), or the opposite – very 'stiff and tight' (hypomobile).

The *hyper*mobile person, generally speaking, has greater than normal mobility around all of their body's joints. 'Hyper' means 'in excess', so by definition these people have 'excess mobility' in the joints of their body. Hypermobile people were often called 'double jointed' in the schoolyard. At the extreme end of hypermobility are the body contortionists you see on talent shows and performing as circus acts. They can perform bizarre and often disturbing movements with their impossibly mobile joints – for example, the feet behind the head and head between the legs type of tricks that intrigue, perplex and, at times, disgust us. However, not everyone who inherits hypermobility around their joints has this degree of movement.

Hypermobile people are characterised by several body traits, such as the ability to bend their thumb towards their forearm, hyperextend their knees and elbows, and bend forwards and put their hands on the ground. Naturally hypermobile children tend to do very well in and enjoy sports such as swimming and gymnastics where a high level of movement around joints is favourable. Because of this large movement range around the joints, in my practice I affectionately refer to such people as 'floppies'. That is, their joints are often just that – very floppy!

It is worth noting that you can be a hypermobile person but still have very tight specific muscle groups. For example, it's not uncommon for the hypermobile runner to still have tight running muscle groups such as the gluts, calves, hamstrings, quadriceps and hip flexors, while at a joint level exhibiting large ranges of motion due to their genetically determined hypermobility.

In contrast, the *hypo*mobile person is characterised by less than normal movement around the joints of their body. For example, on testing they have difficulty getting anywhere near touching their toes, cannot hyperextend their elbows or knees and, when flexing their thumb, it does not get anywhere near their forearm. Hypomobile children often gravitate towards and find natural ability in sports such as football and other contact sports. In my practice I (again affectionately) refer to such people as 'stiffies' because they don't bend much – they are 'stiff'.

It is also possible to be in the middle of the mobility scale. That is, you may not be hypermobile or hypomobile; rather, your overall joint movement range is somewhere in between. I refer to these people as 'flippies'. I estimate through my clinical observations that 20 to 30 per cent of the population are flippies, with approximately 30 per cent being stiffies and 30 per cent being floppies.

In addition to floppies, stiffies, and flippies, a condition known as benign joint hypermobility syndrome (BJHMS) exists, and people with this condition are at the extreme end of joint hypermobility. People who have BJHMS have connective tissue disorders, whereby the tissue that holds 'things' together in the body are defective. The result is extreme mobility that creates joint pain and symptoms. BJHMS is distinct from people who are hypermobile in that, although hypermobile people have joints that move through greater than normal ranges of motion, they do not experience joint-related pains or symptoms.

Children naturally have a greater range of motion than fully developed adults, with the prevalence of hypermobility in children being reported to be as high as 30 per cent.[1] Unfortunately, such mobile children are more susceptible to joint sprains, growth-related pains and, at times, back pain, and do often go on to experience a greater incidence of injuries through their years of growth into adulthood. It's important to note, however, that the presence of hypermobility of the joints in children does not equate to having BJHMS.

It's also worth noting that it is more common for females to have more joint mobility than males at any given age. Additionally, as we mature in years, we all become 'tighter' with smaller joint ranges of motion.

The impact of joint hypermobility can be problematic for runners. Unless the greater than normal joint movement ranges of the hypermobile runner can be stabilised, the runner is at greater risk of succumbing to injury.

What's your mobility status?

Understanding what mobility status you have been genetically equipped with is vitally important. In practice, when coaching injured runners towards pain- and injury-free running, I use several relatively quick tests to determine the runner's mobility status.

A formal evaluation method often used clinically is the Beighton's scale, which uses nine tests and scores each one. The scale looks at movement around the little finger, thumb, elbow, knees, and trunk bend. Both sides are tested, with a higher score representing a higher degree of inherited mobility.

In my practice working with injured runners, I find using the Beighton scale cumbersome and too time-consuming. Although I use some of the same tests as the Beighton Scale, I don't perform all nine tests and score each of the tests.

Instead, my preference is to have the runner perform the following movements:

1   Make a limp wrist and with the other hand push the thumb as close to the forearm as possible. I observe the degree of movement, or how close the thumb gets to the forearm. The closer the thumb gets, the more genetic mobility is normally present.

2   Extend their arm at the elbow. I apply a degree of overpressure and take the arm into full extension. I am looking for how much 'hyper extension' there may be with this movement at the runner's elbow.

3   Ask the runner to stand and see if they can hyperextend their knees. I am looking for the degree of hyperextension present. This is very obvious and will easily be observed.

All of these tests are completed on both sides of the runner's body, because runners can have side to side differences in mobility. This is important to note at the start of the injury proofing process.

To test your mobility status at home, try the following six movements:

1   Bend forwards to put your hands flat on the floor keeping your legs straight.

2   See if you can hyperextend your knees while standing.

3   See how far back you can pull all of your toes.

4   With a floppy wrist, see how close you can get your thumb towards the inside of your forearm. Use the other hand to guide the thumb towards the forearm.

5   See how far backwards you can bend all of your fingers.

6   See if you can hyper-extend your elbows.

If you have flexibility in the majority of the movements (for example, you can get your thumb close to your forearm and put your palms flat on the floor when bending forward), you likely have a hypermobile body. Remember you can be genetically hypermobile but still tight in key running muscle groups such as the quadriceps, calves and hamstrings.

How mobility affects a runner's body and maintenance efforts

Discovering your genetically determined mobility status is of high importance in your quest to run pain and injury free. If you know your genetic mobility status, you are able to more specifically direct your efforts towards body maintenance.

Body maintenance for a runner is body 'upkeep'. Just as you need to maintain a home with regular cleaning and repairs, you also need to maintain a runner's body.

Most runners perform some degree of a 'body maintenance' routine – perhaps a set of exercises or stretches that they routinely do. Often times, these exercises have not been prescribed by a health professional and are instead often an amalgamation of exercises that the runner has either been shown to do by a running friend, observed other runners doing, or simply discovered themselves. The problem with this approach is that the exercises being performed may not be the exercises that the runner will actually benefit from. They are not specific or individualised to match the needs of their running body.

Broadly speaking, a hypermobile runner needs to focus more on stability and strength type exercises, in order to counteract their excessive joint mobility. When the hypermobile runner's body is put under stress from the loads associated with regular running training, the risk of injury is heightened due to poor joint stability.

In contrast, the hypomobile runner needs to put more emphasis on exercises that stretch tight joints and muscle groups.

Just as a hypermobile runner's body will encounter excessive loads (in their case due to the excessive mobility), so too will the hypomobile runner's body – this time due to excessive or adverse muscular tightness around their joints. The stretching serves to reduce joint loading and decrease the likelihood of a given joint being overloaded and injured. Stretching of tight muscle groups also allows the body to move through greater ranges of motion with less resistance. The ability to have joints move through full and unencumbered ranges of motion is very important for runners seeking to run faster, and pain and injury free.

The effects of mobility status on a runner's body and their required body maintenance routines are summarised in the following table.

	The hypermobile runner	**The hypomobile runner**
Needs to	Stabilise their joints	Stretch tight muscle groups
Good exercise modes	> Home exercise program that focuses on strength and stability exercises > Pilates (floor and/or Pilates reformers) > Whole body vibration (e.g. Galileo) > Gym program (strength training)	> Home program that focuses on stretching and mobility > Yoga > Pilates (floor and/or Pilates reformers) > Foam roller exercises

	The hypermobile runner	**The hypomobile runner**
Is at risk of	Injuries due to excessive mobility: > acute sprains (e.g. ankle sprains) > knee ligament injuries if the body is subjected to heavy loads from trauma (e.g. a fall) > progressive onset of overuse injures due to weakness around joints (e.g. shin splints)	Overuse injuries due to muscular tightness around joints and the resultant excessive loads produced: > runner's knee > Achilles tendon pain > ITB friction syndrome

Ultimately, the benefits of completing exercises specific to your body's mobility status are:

> less likelihood of developing running injuries and associated pain

> more time efficiency because the exercises are more targeted

> faster running.

Looking for unsafe components in your running 'chassis'

In addition to being aware of your body's genetically determined mobility status, you also need to discover or identify your body's potential 'problem areas'. Discovering how your body fares with key running physical attributes is analogous to a safety check on a car. In this case, you are looking for any defects that your body (chassis) may have that, unless fixed, make running over a period of time unsafe.

You can check for potential problem areas of the body by benchmarking key running-specific movements and ranges of motion against a set of reference scores. In physio parlance, we call this performing a running screening.

The purpose of performing a running screening is to:

1   Identify problem or potential problem areas of the body. For example, tight hamstrings or quadriceps may lead to knee pain, tight claves may lead to Achilles tendon problems, and reduced hip external rotation range will contribute to any lower limb injury.

2   Allow for a specific home exercise program to be developed for the runner that will reduce the likelihood of injury development and increase a runner's efficiency.

3   Have a set of data for your body at the beginning of this five step process that will allow for quantification of your progress towards pain- and injury-free running.

The running screening

In my practice, I take runners through a series of eight tests to determine their baseline data for several key measurements. Each of these measures can then be compared with scores that are the preferred scores for runners.

Each of the eight tests is a key physical measure that allows for the identification of injury risk factors, and the identification of any areas that can be targeted to help a runner run faster.

For example, if hip external rotation (one of the tests measured in a running screening) is measured as being less than the preferred range, a prescribed strengthening program can correct the runner's score. Through following the prescribed program and improving the hip external rotation score, the runner will experience faster and improved running efficiency.

The running screening is comprised of the following eight tests:

1   Calf muscle length

2   Quadriceps length

3   Hamstrings length

4   Hip flexor length

5   Thoracic spine extension Range of Motion (ROM) – combined elevation test

6   Hip stability – single-leg squat control test

7   Hip stability – hip active external rotation test

8   Core stability – side bridge endurance hold test

The appendix includes an example of the running screening that I use in my practice in order to discover the attributes of a runner's body. I've also included information on what this screening reveals, and exercises you can then do to improve any potentially problematic body attributes uncovered by the screening. Refer to www.pogophysio.com.au/book-resources to view a video of a running screening.

Note: Even with a willing and able partner the running screening tests are difficult to perform at home by yourself. In order to get an accurate assessment of your body, and obtain accurate and meaningful data, I suggest engaging the services of a trained physiotherapist. The running screening provided in the appendix shows you the tests you can run through with your physio. Take this book to them and have them complete the running screening table in the appendix. If you don't already have a physio, ask for recommendations from other runners you know or do an online search for reputable sports physios in your local area.

After your running screening has been performed a tailored home exercise program can be prescribed. The benefits of a tailored home exercise program are many. A tailored home exercise will allow you to get maximum body results with the minimum input of time and effort.

Body maintenance – panel-beat your chassis

Hopefully you are now aware of your genetic endowment with regards to your mobility status. If you've completed your running screening with a physio, you should also now be aware of your body's strengths and weaknesses. As a result you also have a tailored set of exercises that will assist you in keeping your measures within ideal parameters. All of this will make you a less injury prone and ultimately a faster runner.

What follows this body discovery process is the need to maintain and look after your running body with an ongoing focus and intent. Looking after your running body should include regular completion of your home exercise program combined with regular body 'tissue' work, and maintenance of your body within or close to its ideal frame weight (see the following section 'Discovering your ideal frame weight' for more on this).

Tissue work refers to any form of therapy that assists your body's tissues in staying healthy. In my practice, I lightheartedly refer to this as the need to 'panel-beat' your chassis. That is, you need to iron out the kinks and 'buff and polish' your body. This is necessary to ensure you get the most out of your body's potential performance and also key to remaining injury free by way of having 'healthy tissues'.

Tissue therapies may include the manual (hands-on) therapies of physiotherapy, osteopathy, myotherapy, chiropractic or remedial massage. As a physiotherapist, I regularly conduct 'panel-beating' or 'maintenance' sessions for runners of all levels.

During these sessions I may use a combination of the following techniques to ensure the runner is getting the most out of their body:

> *Massage therapy.* Used on all major running muscle groups, including legs, gluts, lower back, breathing muscles, and upper back and neck muscles.

> *Joint mobilisations.* Used on joints that require smooth and maximal movement ranges, such as joints of the feet, ankles, knees, hips and back.

> *Joint manipulations.* Typically for stiffness between the shoulder blades – the thoracic spine of runners regularly gets stiff from repetitive loading from the impact forces of running.

> *Dry needling/acupuncture.* Used to release active muscle trigger points.

Most runners – and people in general – recognise massage therapy and the above-mentioned manual therapy techniques or methods as being beneficial. Excitingly, research has verified that manual therapy has great benefits. The benefits of receiving regular tissue work have been shown to include the following:

> reduces muscle soreness

> flushes toxins and lactic acid from the body

> reduces strains on joints

> assists recovery after a sporting event

> promotes relaxation

> promotes less 'stress'

> improves circulation

> improves lymphatic fluid circulation

> reduces DOMS (delayed onset of muscle soreness) following hard bouts of exercise.

> softens fascia (the connective tissue within the body)

> removes adhesions between the muscle and fascia (places where the two stick together and restrict movement)

> increases the number of lymphocytes (white blood cells that play a key role in fighting infection)

> decreases levels of cortisol (the 'stress' hormone linked to chronic inflammation)

> curbs chronic disease.

In fact during one recent university study looking at the possible benefits of massage, researchers were so compelled by their findings that they actually made receiving a massage a regular part of their weekly routine.

Just as the researchers found positive benefits of massage therapy, I too observe runners who get regular tissue work do better in terms of performance and injury minimisation than those runners who do not invest or make time for regular tissue work.

You will need to find a therapist you are both comfortable and happy with and make receiving regular 'panel-beating' a part of your training routine. It's every bit as important as your next training run. The key is discovering your body's pattern of when it needs and responds best to such body-maintenance sessions.

The frequency of the maintenance sessions will vary for every runner. Having an awareness of your mobility status and your chassis weaknesses will allow you to find a rhythm of body maintenance that will be of greatest benefit to you.

However, as a general rule:

> If you are a hypermobile runner, you will need to receive tissue work in order to address muscular tightness

that has developed in key muscle groups as a result of compensation for the excessive movements of your joints. For example, hamstrings often develop adverse tightness due to weak and ineffective gluteals. Even though a hypermobile runner's muscles will typically be lower in tone than a hypomobile runner's muscles, the overcompensation of certain muscles groups that are compensating for weak muscle groups creates adverse tension in these compensating muscles, which requires tissue work.

> If you are a hypomobile runner, your inherent tightness and naturally higher tone musculature will require body tissue work to allow for optimal function of your joints and limbs. The higher tone/tension of a hypomobile runner's muscles can be well managed through regular tissue work combined with a targeted home exercise program.

The regularity of your body maintenance and tissue needs will be related to your training volume, your natural running ability, and any event preparations you are undertaking. The following table provides a guide for the frequency of body work.

	Weekly volume	Tissue work maintenance schedule
Beginner	10–30kms	Every 10–12 weeks
Intermediate	30–60kms	Monthly
Advanced	60–100kms+	Weekly or fortnightly

The following provides a summary of the benefits of body maintenance and tissue work for the runner:

> faster running – optimal body function and greater fitness gains due to not being injured

> reduced injury risk

> money saved as a result of fewer injuries and fewer missed events

> greater enjoyment of life and running.

Over the years I have consistently observed that runners who receive regular tissue work experience fewer injuries compared to those who do not get regular tissue work. One of the by-products of being injured less is more consistency in training, which then fuels better running performance. As runners we all want to run faster. Sadly, many runners are unaware of the need for body maintenance and end up injured and never able to fulfil their running potential.

Discovering your ideal frame weight

In addition to discovering your genetic mobility status, chassis weaknesses, and body maintenance needs, you also need to discover your body's ideal 'frame' weight.

Being overweight is often an overlooked causative factor of injury. It is important for any runner to realise that any surplus weight they are carrying on their body will result in increased and often avoidable loading of their body's tissues.

In my practice, I prefer to use the phrase 'frame weight' as opposed to extra body weight. One of the definitions of a frame is 'the way in which something is put together'. In terms of our bodies, the bulk and mass of muscle, fat and other tissues sitting on our skeletons is the way we are 'put together'. Collectively this tissue bulk and our skeletons sum to give us our total frame weight.

I spend time sensitively educating injured runners that their body weight may be a contributing factor to their injury development. I have found that most runners are unaware of the impact that extra kilograms can have on their body and their desire to run pain and injury free. Often they don't consider that the extra weight can contribute to the development of and rate of recovery from running injuries.

The discovery of a runner's ideal frame weight gives them a host of benefits related to not only their running but also their general health and wellbeing.

The 'frame weight' concept

The 'frame weight' concept is not a researched theory, nor is it a concept that is taught in university physiotherapy schools, or, to my knowledge, any other medical university program. Rather the frame weight concept is an observation that I have made throughout the years of my clinical practice as a physio.

Everybody has a different body, a unique body, no two bodies are exactly the same. As a result, I believe that everyone's body has a set operating body weight or weight range, at which I believe they are designed to optimally function. If the individual operates within this ideal range of weight or exact weight, they will experience improved performance due to improved efficiency of movement. The individual will also experience fewer injuries as a result of lessened adverse loading on the joints and tissues. This applies to not only running-related injuries but other injuries such as lower back pain, and the development of joint osteoarthritis in weight-bearing joints such as the hips, knees, and feet.

I believe this ideal frame weight is a genetically determined physical attribute. My thoughts are that a set operating weight range is 'hard wired' into the DNA of every human – that is, that all human beings are born with a weight that their fully matured body should grow to. If the adult body can operate at a weight range in tune with their ideal frame weight, the body will according to my observations operate free from adverse joint and limb loading, and will operate with ease and efficiency.

This frame weight is like a 'set point' of a thermostat. The set point controls the temperature of the room, while the set point of our body weight largely determines the effectiveness of our human movements. This set point may be a number or it may in fact be a range of weights. Given that trial and error is the only way to find your ideal frame weight, I lean more towards the more achievable concept of discovering your ideal frame weight range as opposed to a defined specific number.

A runner who is carrying surplus kilograms in excess of their body's frame weight will be subject to extra stresses and loads. The loading that results from this excess weight tends to be adverse in nature, because the body's skeleton, muscles, connective tissues, ligaments and tendons are put under extra strain by the surplus body weight.

As an example, imagine a runner who has an extra 10 kilograms on their frame. That is akin to putting a 10-kilogram weight in your pocket and running, or running with two bags of potatoes in tow. We know that the impact loading of running is somewhere in the vicinity of two to three times our body weight. However, this normal impact loading range will be increased if the runner is carrying surplus frame weight of 10 kilograms.

So while the impact loading is now higher, the runner's tissues and skeleton has been designed to withstand a certain frame weight range. The gap between the frame weight it is designed to carry and the frame weight the body is carrying equates to the extra and adverse loading. It's where many problems in terms of injury contribution can emanate from.

Don't dodge it

Many health practitioners avoid conversations about surplus body weight because of the sensitivity and perceived awkwardness that may result. Discussing surplus body weight is never an easy conversation to have in the physio consulting room.

Whenever I am tempted to 'dodge' the topic of body weight for an injured runner, I remind myself that my job is to be effective and deliver on the outcome that I am being engaged to deliver on. My role is not to be just liked by my client. There is a huge difference between being liked and being effective. However, being liked and effective don't need to be mutually exclusive when the practitioner is sensitive and caring in their approach.

A runner's recovery from injury will be delayed if they are carrying surplus body weight. If all other injury contributory factors are addressed through an injury rehabilitation program but the excess frame weight is not addressed, the runner remains at risk of further injury or re-aggravation.

Note that it is possible to 'be fit' but still have your frame weight in excess of your ideal frame weight. In such a situation, you're still putting yourself at a greater risk of injury because of the excess weight.

Running and being fit will have a positive effect on a runner's frame weight, but other strategies may still be needed to help get you down to your ideal frame weight. In the following section, I share with you some of these strategies.

It's important to also note that being under your ideal frame weight can create challenges for a runner's body. Although the effects of being under your ideal frame weight are less deleterious to a runner's quest to run pain and injury free, problems can still arise. Conditions such as osteopenia (loss of bone mineral density) and amenorrhoea (female runners losing their regular menstrual cycle) can be the result of running with a frame weight less than the ideal frame weight.

The consequences of any extra kilograms on somebody's frame are not only relevant for the onset, management and recovery from running-related injuries, but extend to general health and wellbeing. It is well documented that surplus body weight markedly increases the risk of lifestyle diseases such as cardiac events, type 2 diabetes and stroke. Being overweight is also one of the major drivers for lower back pain, and the development of osteoarthritis of the knees and hips.

Discovering your ideal frame weight

Unfortunately, there is no easy way to calculate or discover your ideal frame weight. There is no formula that produces the range of body weight or the 'magic' set weight point that a runner needs to operate at or within.

I recommend two methods to arrive at your ideal frame weight:

1   Think back to a time when you were pain and injury free. You had no or very little day-to-day aches or pains. Perhaps you weren't running in your past but that doesn't matter. Reflect on a time when you physically felt healthy and well. Don't over-analyse or complicate the reflection by rationalising things like your fitness, age or lifestyle. Just recall the time when you were uninjured and strong. Now see if you can recall or approximate the body weight you were at that stage. The chances are that this body weight is close to your ideal frame weight. Typically with the kilogram creep experienced by most people with the passing of the years, this weight will be anywhere from 5 to 30 kilograms less than their current body weight.

2   Start to record your body weight and match it to your pain and injury profile. This is not a quick or overnight exercise but rather a commitment required over the course of one to three years. Because of the required time frame for this analysis, most people prefer method 1 – reflecting on their past.

Whatever method you use, make it your aim to start to work your way towards your approximate ideal frame weight. Don't procrastinate – start today. There are no overnight shortcuts. I suggest just start by making some seemingly small daily choices – over time these choices will sum to something significant.

Much had been written on body weight management. I suggest looking for resources that may help you or, if necessary, engaging professional help.

To get you started on your journey towards your ideal frame weight try some of the following tips:

> Break your day into quarters. For example, if you wake at 6 am and go to bed at 10 pm, that is a 16-hour day. In this case, the quarters would be 6 to 10 am, 10 am to 2 pm, 2 to 6 pm, and 6 to10 pm. Rather than attempting to make wise food choices over the course of the entire day, break the day into smaller segments (quarters). You will have more control and motivation to make wise choices when you approach your day in quarters.

> Avoid eating when you are tired. Fatigue can be a real trigger for over indulging.

> Cut out one coffee a day.

> Drink mineral water as a treat as opposed to drinking high-calorie soft drinks.

> Substitute high-sugar drinks such as fruit juice for water.

> Have more salads than calorie-rich meals.

> Decrease the size of your protein ingestion. Try limiting protein intake to portions that are the size of the palm of your hand.

> Be aware of visual cues. For example, smaller plates will mean smaller calorie ingestion, while taller and skinnier glasses will ensure you drink less.

> Place nutritious foods at eye level in your fridge and pantry. You tend to eat the most of what you see first.

> Progressively reduce the size of your meals and portion sizes. Replace your standard dinner plate size with a smaller plate size.

> Don't fear hunger pains. Contrary to popular belief hunger pains do not escalate until you are rolling on the ground clutching your stomach. Rather they actually go away completely after a period of several hours. Few people ever push through the sensation of needing to eat to discover this.

> Chew your food fully before swallowing. Not only does this habit significantly improve digestion but it also creates a margin of time for the 'full reflex' to be sent to your brain, which will result in fewer calories being ingested.

> Reduce or eliminate your intake of bread. Bread is heavily packed with calories.

Be sure to not make your effort to return to your ideal frame weight too stringent or rigid. Pick two or three of the preceding tips and monitor your progress over time. You will be amazed at the results that wise and small daily choices can produce.

Check out the key points from this chapter and then you are ready for step two – running with great technique!

Step 1: Discover your running body – key points

Here are the main points to take away from this chapter:

> Discovering your body's genetic mobility status, physical attributes, maintenance cycle, and ideal frame weight are the necessary first steps in your quest to run pain and injury free.

> You need a documented starting point – a 'Point A'. Step 1 serves at this starting point, from which your progress with the five steps can be evaluated.

> Irrespective of whether genetics appear to have been kind or cruel to you, your aim should still be to run pain and injury free. This aim is absolutely achievable if the five steps are followed, even with seemingly less than ideal inherited genetic traits.

> A running screening will discover any areas of your body that may become problematic or become potential contributing factors of injury.

> As a general rule, hypermobile runners will need to spend more time and energy stabilising and strengthening their bodies in order to avoid injury and improve performance. Alternately, hypomobile runners will benefit from an approach that focuses more on the stretching of tight muscle groups and the promotion of body mobility.

Step 1: Discover your running body – key points (continued)

> It is important to optimise your performance and decrease injury risk by receiving regular body maintenance or tissue work. Sticking to a regular maintenance approach will ultimately save you time, money, and frustration caused by less than optimal running performances. As a general rule, the more you run the more frequent your maintenance cycle should be.

> Be aware that your body has an ideal 'frame weight'. If you run for long enough in surplus of your ideal frame weight, you are putting your body at significant risk of developing an injury. Take the time to discover your ideal frame weight range and aim to maintain this body weight in order to realise your true running potential.

Case studies: Nick and Michelle

Nick (knee pain)

Nick first presented to the practice with quite advanced knee pain of both knees. At the time of Nick's first consultation, Nick reported that he was running three to four times per week. However, Nick was unable to run without considerable pain. He was also experiencing

Nick (knee pain) (continued)

pain squatting down and getting out of chairs and his car. As is often the case with males in pain, Nick put off coming to see me for as long as he possibly could! An upcoming family trip to the snow and the desire to be able to ski pain-free was a great motivator for Nick to take action.

Nick discovered his running body through the initial assessment process, which included a running screening. Nick learnt that he was genetically a hypermobile runner who lacked some of the stability and strength around his hip and core muscles needed to run pain and injury free. In addition, Nick had extreme muscle tightness of the key muscles that surrounded the knee: the quadriceps, hamstrings and calves.

Physiotherapy was commenced which focused on reducing the marked muscle tightness around Nick's knees, the restoration of normal knee cap (patella) movements, promotion of hip and core stability, and the initial modification of Nick's run training program. It was also pointed out to Nick that he was likely between five and ten kilograms above his ideal frame weight and if this extra weight could be shifted, he would be giving himself the best chance of experiencing pain- and injury-free running.

Arthroscopic day surgery was required to 'clean up' the quite damaged medial meniscii (shock absorbers) of both of Nick's knees. However, due to Nick's diligence with his physio rehabilitation, within eight weeks after surgery Nick went off and enjoyed a relatively pain-free trip to the snow. At this stage, Nick was reluctant to run and had been avoiding it, fearful of a return of his previous pain.

Nick (knee pain) (continued)

One year on, Nick had stripped down to his ideal frame weight, and has returned to his normal (pre-pain) running levels. The best part is that Nick is now able to run pain and injury free. As an added bonus Nick's previously irritable lower back pain has also completely resolved.

Michelle (chronic Achilles pain)

Michelle presented with ongoing problematic Achilles tendon pain. The pain had been present for over one year, and at the time of first seeing me, Michelle reported having no success with a variety of previous treatment modalities and self-help strategies. Michelle's personal trainer and fitness coach advised her to seek my opinion.

The driving motivation for Michelle to see me was that she was no longer able to run. This was interfering with her ability to achieve her weight loss and personal training goals.

On assessment, I discovered that Michelle's Achilles tendon was very 'unhappy'. Scans of the tendon via ultrasound revealed the tendon was quite degenerate and extremely aggravated.

Michelle's running screening revealed that Michelle was a hypomobile runner who was very tight across all three of the key lower limb muscles: calf, hamstrings, and quadriceps. Michelle was also approximately 30 to 35 kilograms over her ideal frame weight.

Over the course of the next five months, corrective measures were implemented in order to address the tight calf and lower limb muscles. In addition, Michelle set about reducing her frame weight.

Michelle (chronic Achilles pain) (continued)

By the end of the five months, Michelle had made a successful return to pain-free running, was enjoying and getting great results from her personal training sessions, and was making significant reductions to her frame weight. These results were made possible because the frame weight concept was addressed and acted on early in the rehabilitation process. Michelle learnt to understand her running body limitations and the corrective steps required to enjoy pain-free running.

By Michelle's own report the best part of her return to pain-free running was the positive example she was having on her teenage daughter, a budding junior triathlete.

Chapter 6

STEP 2: Run with great technique

Step 1: Discover your running body

Step 2: Run with great technique

Step 3: Navigate the footwear maze

Step 4: The importance of hip stability

Step 5: The power of rest

After working through step one (refer to chapter 5), you should now have documented your starting position on the five step journey. You hopefully now know your genetic mobility status, the results of your running screening, your approximate body maintenance cycle, and have started to think about identifying your ideal frame weight.

The second step towards pain- and injury-free, and faster running is running with great technique. This step is of high importance for all runners, from beginners through to the elite. Sadly though, this step is often overlooked by aspiring runners. Quite simply, if you wish to run to your fullest potential, running with great technique is critical.

The importance of running technique

Athletes in every sport devote enormous time and energy to perfecting and fine-tuning their sport-specific technique. Without continual improvement of technique and an ongoing quest for perfect 'form', the athlete will never reach their true athletic potential. Nor will they ever perform at their optimal level.

Irrespective of the sport or game, technique improvement must be a continual and ongoing focus. Consider a tennis player or golfer, and the number of hours they practise hitting balls and refining their technique. The very best tennis players and golfers in the world hire coaches to give them continual feedback on their technique and performance.

We all want to run faster and most people train with this focus – largely and sadly ignoring their running technique, and how it could be improved. Very few runners ever schedule a 'practice session' to improve their technique. Recreational and amateur runners will openly confess to seldom giving their running form or technique a thought.

Instead, pulling on the running shoes and heading off for a run, concentrating on the training distance at hand, is the normal cognitive process for most runners. The focus is on the more traditional methods to improve their running speed and fitness: either logging more kilometres, or 'training harder' at a greater intensity.

Seldom is running thought of as a learned skill. Ignoring the importance of technique in a run training program may appear to be nothing more than a small oversight. After all, we can all run, correct? We've been doing it for almost as long as we could walk. However, how we run 'naturally' doesn't necessarily make it 'correct'. Because you have been running since childhood, you may not realise that you can actually change the way you run.

The concept of being deliberate about 'how' we run isn't a natural one. Many people believe that runners have their own unique style of running, with some runners naturally looking better than others. Not recognising that there is skill in the technique of the better runners is a common error.

Running requires a delicate mix of control, balance, stability, timing, and arm and leg co-ordination. Better runners do not just have natural gifts, they also spend time focusing on their running technique. Although running does occur naturally, running with great technique must be practised and it can be learned.

The problem for runners who ignore their technique is that continued running with poor technique over time will likely culminate in injury and lost potential in their running performance.

A runner without any knowledge of good running technique will experience greater loads on their body, run with less efficiency and therefore run more slowly than they otherwise could. So doing a 'stocktake' of how you run (your running technique) is an imperative step in running pain and injury free, and faster. Once you discover how you are running, the focus moves toward running with more efficiency. Running with more efficiency will reduce adverse loads on the body and promote improved performance.

So you want to get faster?

Before we take a look at how to get faster by way of improving your technique, we need to consider the three ways by which a runner can get faster.

The three ways to develop faster running are covered in the following sections.

Increase your aerobic capacity

Increasing your aerobic capacity can be achieved through training. Most runners are unaware that a ceiling or 'genetic cap' exists as to just how far you can train and improve your body's aerobic capacity.

Your aerobic capacity is your body's natural 'engine'. You often hear runners refer to certain runners as having a 'big engine'. What they are in fact referring to is the genetically determined 'aerobic capacity' that a runner is born with. In science terms, this aerobic capacity is referred to as the V02max, which is a measure of the amount of oxygen that can be utilised by the body as a function of the body's weight.

The V02max score is generally considered one of the best indicators of endurance capacity and aerobic fitness. V02max is expressed a number – for example, 70 ml/kg/min. World-class runners would generally have V02max scores above 70ml/kg/min, while your average 70-kilogram, moderately fit male may have a V02max of somewhere between 50 and 60ml/kg/min.

In 2007, in what was one of the first attempts to study the dominant and uberfast Kenyan runners while at the peak of their 'powers', Spanish scientists were able to test and analyse the then world cross country and half-marathon champion Zersenay Tadese. Tadese's V02max was reported to be a very high 83ml/kg/min.[1] While this is a very high score, sporting legend has it that a world-class cross country skier was once measured as having a V02max of 96ml/kg/min. Is this true or even possible? I suspect it may be but only with some 'artificial' assistance.

Women have smaller VO2max scores, which is the chief determinant in the difference in performance for endurance sports between male and female athletes.

The best way to calculate VO2max is by analysis in a controlled setting such as a laboratory. Access to this equipment is usually only found at universities. Online V02max calculators can convert exercise intensity level (as measured by heart rate) to a score of V02max. While these online calculators are not as accurate as laboratory testing, they can serve as a guide for runners interested in approximating their V02max.

V02max itself does not guarantee performance, but it is certainly a key element of a runner's potential. The runner with the highest V02max is not always destined to be the winner – a runner with a lesser V02max beating a runner who has a higher V02max is possible and a likely common occurrence.

Elevate your lactate or 'anaerobic' threshold

When it comes to performance and faster running, being able to run at a high intensity before lactate acid production occurs and running with good economy are also important considerations.

Unlike a runner's genetically determined maximum aerobic capacity, a runner has a large scope to positively change their 'anaerobic threshold'. 'Anaerobic' simply means without oxygen, and 'threshold' is when a certain point is reached – in this case, the point where lactic acid begins to flood muscle cells at a greater rate than it can be removed. In other words, the build-up of lactate acid occurs with exercise intensity above a runner's anaerobic threshold.

If you have ever felt the 'burn' while running, you have hit or exceeded your anaerobic threshold. You will have experienced that once you 'feel the burn', it becomes impossible to sustain speed, power, and efficiency. Once this feeling kicks in, it's a downwards spiral of performance.

The anaerobic threshold is expressed as percentage of V02max. So if your anaerobic threshold is 70 per cent, you will start to develop a build-up of lactic acid when you're exercising at 70 per cent of your maximal oxygen utilisation (V02max). Alternately, in the absence of a known V02max, the anaerobic threshold can be estimated as a percentage of maximal heart rate. Take the example of a 40 year old runner:

> Maximal heart rate: 220 beats per min (bpm) – age = 180bpm

> Estimated anaerobic threshold (occurring at 70 per cent of maximal heart rate): 0.7 × 180bpm = 126bpm

So if this runner exercised at a level that saw their heart rate exceed 126bpm, they would be close to producing lactate acid and subsequently needing to slow down, and lessen the intensity of the training run.

Elevating your anaerobic threshold can be achieved through what is known as 'anaerobic threshold' training. Anaerobic threshold training conditions your body to delay the point at which it begins producing lactic acid. Such training can include fartlek and interval running, whereby the runner trains at faster than race pace (that is at or above the anaerobic threshold) with interspersed rests.

Once the body begins producing lactic acid, it begins a process of slowing the runner down. At some point, the runner is forced to stop. So, the higher the 'threshold' can be elevated, the longer the runner will be able to sustain a fast pace while training or racing.

Improve your running economy through better running technique

A runner's aim should be to use or expend as little fuel as possible at any given running speed. This is what is known as running economy or running 'efficiency'. (For the purposes of this chapter, I will stick with the more traditionally used term of running economy.)

Running economy is analogous to an automobile's fuel economy. A car with good fuel economy can sustain a given speed and use less fuel than a car with poor fuel economy. As car consumers, we all want cars that have great fuel economy. As runners, we should have the same desire: to be runners who run economically. Running with great technique is the chief enabler of running economy and is the focus of this chapter.

Technique improvements allow a runner to run faster and use less fuel because they have become more efficient or economical as a result of improving their technique. Simply stated, running economy is about getting more 'bang for the buck'. It's about getting the most forward movement for the least amount of energy expended.

In 2007, Zersenay Tadese was reported to have what was at the time one of the best running economies ever measured.[2] Tadese used less oxygen at a given running speed than any runner who was tested before him. The researchers recorded the total volume of oxygen Tadese used to run one kilometre measured in ml/kg/km. Tadese used just 150ml/kg/km while running at 3:06/km pace. In comparison, Frank Shorter (the 1972 Munich Olympic marathon hero who spawned the first running boom – refer to chapter 3) was recorded as using

196ml/kg/km at 3:06/km pace while elite Caucasian runners were recorded as using 211ml/kg/km running at 3:09/km pace.

Running economy is influenced by both physiological and biomechanical factors. In step one (chapter 5), we looked at the effect that our genetic mobility status and our body shape can have on our running performance. Tadese's incredible running economy was partly attributed to the small size of his calves relative to the other elite Spanish runners included in the study who had larger calves.[3] However, it was not only Tadese's calf size that resulted in his superior running economy. Tadese's smooth and elegant running technique was also another key factor for his incredible running economy.

Over the last two decades, several running technique methods have emerged that aim to teach runners how to improve their technique and their subsequent running economy. Two of the most popular methods are the 'Chi Running' and 'POSE' methods.

Chi Running is a method of running developed by Danny Dreyer in 1999 that blends the physical and spiritual ethos of Tai Chi. The method uses the principles of Tai Chi to focus on alignment, relaxation, and proper form when running. The method emphasises posture, core strength, relaxed legs, mindfulness, and a mid-foot landing on impact with the ground.[4] (With a mid-foot landing, the entire foot more or less touches the ground at the same time.)

Meanwhile the POSE method was developed in the 1970s by two-time Olympic athletics coach Dr Nicholas Romanov. The method is similar to Chi Running in that it too teaches technique cues and body positioning with the aim of improving a runner's performance and reducing the runner's injury risk.

The key distinction between the two running technique methods is that the POSE method advocates forefoot striking of the foot on impact. In contrast, the Chi Running method advocates a mid-foot strike.

One other key running technique method that has been popular throughout the last decade is the 'Evolution Running' method. The Evolution Running method is somewhat a hybrid of the POSE and Chi methods, sharing many of the same body positioning concepts, but as with Chi, favouring a mid-foot strike. Evolution Running coach Ken Mierke has said that runners of all levels can improve their economy by somewhere between 4.5 and 8 per cent – simply by improving their technique. Projecting this improvement in running efficiency into real-time gains could equate to a 2 minute and 42 second time saving per hour of running!

Mierke was quoted as saying, 'Differences between runners are consistently due to technique more than to fitness. Faster runners are more fit, but technique plays a greater role in sustained fast running than fitness does'. This statement captures the importance of running with great technique and the associated benefits that such a focus on technique brings.

As you continue in this chapter it is imperative to remember that great runners are born, and then trained. You can do a great deal to improve your running economy and performance by making technique changes.

Let's take a closer look at running with great technique.

Lowering your injury risk through great running technique

In addition to potentially making a runner more economical and therefore faster, running technique can also be a key contributing factor to the onset of the vast majority of running injuries. Chapter 3 outlines how running technique features as a potential chief cause (or contributing factor) for commonly experienced running injuries.

Research has also linked aspects of running technique with injury risk. One study of 45 healthy recreational runners found that subtle increases in the number of steps taken by the runners resulted in substantive reductions in the loading of the hip and knee joints,[5] and therefore a reduced injury risk for the hip and knees of the runners who participated in the study.

Meanwhile, a published case study found that debilitating symptoms of 'compartment syndrome' (pain in the front and outside musculature of the shins) were abolished in two runners who received six weeks of running technique instruction. The runners were a 21-year-old female who had suffered from her symptoms for four years, and a 21-year-old male runner who was seven months post leg surgery and experiencing compartment syndrome symptoms again on the operated leg and also the other leg. The technique modification focused on helping these two runners shift from landing on their heels to landing on their forefoot.[6]

In my practice, I have observed that for the vast majority of recreational and competitive non-elite runners, running technique is commonly one of the key contributing factors for the onset of many running-related injuries. At an elite level, where running technique is generally very good, the contribution of technique being a contributing factor in the onset of injury tends to be less.

In practice, I spend time educating injured runners that their injury has developed due to a combination of contributory or causative factors – as we identified in Chapter 4, rarely is injury the result of a single isolated factor. Much of the 'art' of physiotherapy rehabilitation is the ability of the practitioner to discover all of the contributing factors and address them accordingly. Any factor that is missed will result in the runner not receiving a full and complete rehabilitation.

Poor or improper running technique is one factor that I often observe being neglected or not addressed with running injury rehabilitation programs. This is generally due to a lack of 'awareness' of the importance of technique by the runner, and sometimes also the treating practitioner.

Some practitioners may be unfamiliar with what constitutes good running technique, and so are not equipped to coach an injured runner how to improve their technique in order to facilitate a return to running and a reduced injury risk.

Five key principles of great running technique

There are five key principles that constitute good running technique. The most fluid, graceful, and fastest runners on the planet exhibit these characteristics as part of their running technique.

Even if you're not aspiring to be one of the world's fastest runners, your running speed would be well served by becoming familiar with these five principles. Not only will your running speed improve but the likelihood of developing a running-related injury will markedly decrease.

The five key principles that constitute great running technique are as follows:

1   Do not overstride (run with a good cadence)

2   Minimise bopping up and down (vertical displacement)

3   Optimise foot strike placement (where your foot lands)

4   Optimise your body position

5   Utilise your natural springs (tendons)

The following sections take a closer look at each of these five principles of running with great technique.

Principle 1: Do not overstride

While numerous running technique flaws exist, arguably the major flaw made by most runners is the adoption of an 'overstriding' running style. Based on my clinical observations, I estimate that overstriding is evident in approximately 75 per cent of injured runner's technique. This observation means that three-quarters of the running-related injuries I treat have overstriding as one of the chief contributory factors to the development of the running injury being rehabilitated.

Once you know what to look for, you will observe runners overstriding at any event or during any training run. Overstriding is particularly evident in events that attract beginner and recreational runners. While it's not just beginner runners who overstride, it's far less likely to see overstriding running styles in the ranks of the elite runners.

Before looking at reasons why runners overstride, it's important to clarify what an 'overstride' actually is. Defining a stride as being too 'long' isn't useful, because a runner's stride length will vary, depending on the speed that the runner is running at. So identifying an overstride must be defined in the context of where the foot lands relative to the runner's knee.

When a runner overstrides, their foot at the point of impacting with the ground will land in front of their knee (see following figure). Invariably with the leg in an extended (straightened) position, the runner's heel will typically be the first point of contact. Landing in this out-stretched leg position increases loading on the runner's legs and body, and also slows the runner down.

Many people ask me why runners overstride. I would like to give a simple one-size-fits-all answer. Although no such answer exists, I believe that there are two primary reasons why runners overstride.

The first reason has to do with our own inclinations. It seems 'intuitive' and very 'natural' to take bigger strides in an attempt to run faster. When trying to catch the runner in front of us, our default self-talk is often something like, 'I'm going to stride out and catch them'. That is, if we want to speed up, we default in our thinking to 'I must take bigger strides to go faster' and we begin to do just that – take bigger strides.

What is the rationale for such thinking? Why do we assume that bigger strides will produce faster running? My best hypothesis is that when we observe elite runners running at the front of an Olympic marathon, or any other race in which they compete, we see these runners taking enormously long strides. Typically they do this with ease and make running at fast speeds look effortless.

I believe that when we observe these runners 'loping' along at rapid speeds, we then assume that to run fast we need to take big strides. What we do not realise in adopting this incorrect assumption is that the elite runner's big strides are a *result* of the sheer speed they are running at, and not the *cause* of their fast running speed. Technique factors such as good foot position, forwards body lean and tendon utilisation, combined with the previously mentioned high VO2max scores and elevated lactate thresholds, all positively affect the speed of these elite runners. We typically fail to take these factors into account when we watch the elite runners compete, instead focusing simply on their huge strides and attributing these as the chief reason for their fast running.

I believe the second reason why so many runners overstride has to do with 'motion control' or heavy heeled running shoes. The widespread use of the motion control shoe by the majority of runners in recent decades has, I believe, had an effect on the stride lengths of runners.

Motion control running shoes are designed to absorb shock and stabilise the foot on impact. With such extra cushioning, I believe that some runners can in effect get 'lazy' with their stride length and take longer strides than they normally would. They 'default' to a longer stride length, one in which the first point of contact with the ground is made by the heel, which is positioned at the end of an over extended and straightened leg.

Because the heavy heeled shoe provides extra cushioning, no immediate consequence is felt by the runner when they overstride. The braking forces being 'thrown back' from the ground toward the overstriding runner are largely absorbed by the well-cushioned shoes. As a result, these forces go unnoticed and don't result in any immediate repercussions.

However, if the runner was in a lesser heeled shoe or, at an extreme, attempting to run barefoot, the runner would be less likely to land in an overstriding manner, in which their heel would likely make first contact with the ground. The impact of the heel with the ground would mean the runner would immediately experience discomfort. As a result, the runner would modify their technique away from an overstriding style with an associated heel-strike.

Research validates avoiding overstriding as a sound injury prevention and, in some cases, rehabilitation strategy. The study referenced earlier in this chapter found that when runners decreased their step length by 10 per cent or more, reduced impact loading at the knee (and hip) was achieved.[7] This research finding is significant given that we know that knee injuries are the most prevalent injuries among runners, with nearly 50 per cent of all running injuries occurring at the knee and more than 90 per cent of individuals with patella-femoral (knee cap) pain suffering ongoing or chronic pain.[8,9]

So for runners seeking to run pain and injury free, the good news is that the risk of developing knee pain can be reduced by modifying step rate and length to prevent heel striking. It has also been suggested that running with shorter strides reduced the risk of tibial stress fractures.[10] Hence this may be a great injury prevention strategy.

It's important to note that when a runner transitions from habitual overstriding and a heel-striking technique to an improved running cadence, it can at first feel like 'harder work'. There will be a slight increase in oxygen utilisation when making more leg contact 'cycles', as a function of running with a higher cadence and a shorter stride length.

One research paper caused a stir when it reported that eight triathletes who received 12 weeks of POSE running technique coaching actually had reduced running economy after the 12 weeks[11] when compared with another eight triathletes who did not receive POSE technique coaching.

In the coaching group, the triathletes' stride length reduced from 137.3 centimetres to 129.2 centimetres, which resulted in the runners adopting more of a forefoot landing than a heel-strike landing. Unlike the reduction found in running economy, the shortened stride-length of the participating runners was a positive outcome of the intervention.

However, the results of this isolated research paper could come under some critique. For example, the runners were not tracked beyond twelve weeks to see whether their running economy improved at a later stage due to their shortened stride length.

In correcting the technique of injured runners, I have observed that runners may report a 'perceived' greater effort in taking shorter and quicker steps. I believe this perceived effort reflects the increased attentional focus on the task of running differently and with a new technique, rather than a true metabolic 'cost' of shortening the stride length as was reported by the researchers.

Measuring overstriding

When coaching overstriding injured runners, the best way to start is to begin to count the number of steps (or foot strikes) each minute. This will give the runner their 'cadence' in steps taken per minute (steps/min).

In order to not overstride, you should be aiming to run with a turnover rate (or cadence) of 180 to 184 steps per minute. This is equivalent to one foot contacting the ground around 90 times per minute, or a cadence of 90 (single foot). When your cadence is less than this, you will be typically overstriding.

By running at the correct cadence, your foot will land closer to your body's centre of mass at foot strike. This will look like the foot landing underneath the runner's knee. This is opposed to the foot landing out in front of the knee, which is what occurs when a runner overstrides.

You can measure your running cadence – and work out whether you are overstriding – in two ways. In order of my preference they are:

1 *Do a manual count or 'stocktake' of your cadence when training.* Simply count your steps for one leg over a one-minute interval on your next run. (I recommend counting only one foot because counting a single foot is easier and more accurate than counting both feet.) Use your stopwatch or whatever device you have available to ensure you get an accurate one-minute count. Then begin to count for one minute of every five minutes of running.

   Doing manual step counts creates a 'brain to foot' link that makes integrating 180 to 184 steps/min achievable in the quickest possible time frames. I have found that runners who commit to manually counting one minute out of every five minutes of running tend to improve their cadence more quickly than runners who use technology to get their count (such as GPS watches, etc.).

2 *Use a foot pod.* Some devices (for example, a Garmin or GPS-type device), which are similar to a bike computer, will automatically compute and display your cadence. I encourage runners who wish to use technology to still do the manual count for a period of time in order to achieve a cadence of 180 to 184 steps/min, before using technology to monitor their ongoing cadence.

Most runners report an initial cadence of fewer than 90 single foot steps/minute. This reflects a runner who is taking stride lengths that are 'too long'. Hence, they're unable to get the required number of strides completed inside the assigned one-minute time interval.

When I first started to count my cadence, I was surprised to discover that I was taking 78 steps/min (counting one foot). At first I thought it would be impossible to consistently run with a cadence of 90 steps/min. However, I persevered, and I now run every minute of the many kilometres I cover each week with a cadence that is consistently 92 steps/min.

The role of fatigue

Because running consists of repetitive motions that involve repetitive muscle contractions, the body is subjected to muscular fatigue. When a runner fatigues, such as towards the end of a long training run, the runner's cadence will tend to decrease. As the runner fatigues they can default to taking longer strides as opposed to the more economical shorter strides. At this point of fatigue, the drop in cadence will typically correlate directly with a reduction of speed and a decrease in running economy.

One study found that the incidence of heel striking increased by 5.2 per cent between the 10-kilometre and 32-kilometre markers of a marathon.[12] This likely occurred as a result of the fatigued runners losing their ability to maintain a quick turnover rate of the legs and so they resorted by default to their overstriding and heel striking running style.

Not only can fatigue result in a slowing down of a runner's pace and a loss of form by way of return to overstriding, it can also increase the chance of injury. As fatigue sets in, the protective effect of the muscles' ability to absorb loads is reduced. The effect of a reduction in load absorption by the fatigued muscles is an elevated or increased risk of injury.

Running cadence guide

It's also worth noting that a point exists when extra steps per minute become inefficient. For example, if you ran with a cadence of 100 steps/min or above, you would likely be negatively affecting your running economy, due to the associated extra oxygen debt. An exact cadence for this point of inefficiency is difficult to define; however, it becomes physiologically difficult to exceed 100 steps/min for distance runners.

The table opposite is an easy to use reference guide to interpreting your running cadence.

Increasing your running cadence

You can use a variety of methods to increase your running cadence. It is best to not overcomplicate the process, so I encourage runners to keep their approach simple.

I have observed runners who 'over-think' their approach often delay the gains that can be made, when compared with runners who keep the process simple.

Steps (foot strikes)/min	90 foot strikes /min	<90 foot strikes/min	>90 foot strikes/min
Inter-pretation	Ideal turn-over rate Foot lands directly under knee and body's centre of mass Likely mid-foot landing at impact Better recruitment of gluteals and hamstrings Better use of stored energy in tendons Improved running economy	Overstriding; the runner cannot get enough foot strikes completed per minute The stride length is too long Likely landing heel first Added energy cost to running An increased injury risk	Possibly landing on forefoot instead of mid-foot 'Wheel spinning', which creates an additional energy cost Running economy decreases if taking too many steps/min

Follow these tips to increase your running cadence:

> Be patient. Be prepared for a correction of cadence and overstriding to take up to six months. The longer a runner has run with an overstriding and slow cadence style, the longer it will take to correct. On average, most runners

will have made significant changes at around the three-month mark.

> Irrespective of distance (short, middle, or long runs) count for one minute of every five minutes of running.

> Pay close attention to your cadence as fatigue sets in. The aim is to run at a cadence of 90 steps/min throughout the run's duration. Keeping a cadence of 90 steps/min is extremely important at the end of the run when fatigue kicks in.

> Run like Cliff Young! If you're familiar with the Cliff Young story, think of the famed 'Cliff Young shuffle'. By not overstriding, Cliff Young modelled exceptional running economy, claiming victory in the inaugural 1983 Sydney to Melbourne ultra-marathon. Cliff covered the distance of 875 kilometres as a 61 year old in five days, five hours and fifteen minutes. This extraordinary feat of endurance was not achieved by Cliff running with an overstriding style and too low of a cadence. (If you're not familiar with Cliff Young, search online for 'Cliff Young shuffle'. You will discover this is a heart-warming story of sporting triumph.)

> Count, count, count! Make counting your cadence a habit on every run. Irrespective of whether you are running slow, fast, on a track, on the road, on trails, a long run, or a short run, just count! Consistent counting and habit formation is the key to success.

> Keep in mind that initially trying to increase your cadence can feel less efficient. Rest assured that this feeling of extra

work is only temporary. Inside two to four weeks you will begin to experience the rewards of running with a faster cadence.

> Keep persisting. If you have identified that you are an overstriding runner and you wish to run faster and with less injury risk, you really have no alternative to getting your cadence to 90 single steps/min. If you do, you will reap the rewards of running faster with a far reduced injury risk. Once you have corrected your cadence and ceased overstriding, you will never look back (particularly in a race – there will be no need!).

Principle 2: Minimise bopping up and down

The old maxim 'what goes up must come down' certainly holds true in running. The higher the body launches into the air at the time of push-off, the harder, and with greater impact, the runner's landing will be. Typically a runner experiences two to three times their body weight on landing by way of what is known as ground reaction forces.

Cast your mind back to high school physics and you may recall that for every action there is an equal and opposite reaction. For example, if you were to push someone, the same force that you generate to push someone with will in turn be exerted back onto your body by way of the equal and opposite reaction force. In this example, the equal and opposite force appears to be 'invisible' in that it is absorbed by the pusher's body. In contrast it is easy to detect the force being elicited onto the person who has been pushed, because the person pushed moves.

For runners, the impact with the ground is what the body must 'deal with' in terms of 'invisible' ground reaction forces. These forces are transmitted into the runner's legs and upwards into the body. The impact made may be appropriate, such as with a mid-foot strike, or excessive, such is often the case with a heel-strike. Greater crashing on landing results in greater loads on the runner's body. This in turn heightens the chance of developing an injury.

With too much 'bopping up and down', the runner's body gains excessive amplitude (height) during each stride. The problem with this excessive bopping is that the further up the body travels into the air, the harder it will come crashing down. Greater bopping up and down motion is created by an overstriding running technique.

When a runner is overstriding (with a cadence of fewer than 90 single steps/min), their foot will likely land out in front of their knee and their body's centre of mass at the time of impact with the ground. When this occurs, the ground applies an equal and opposite force back up the runner's leg. This equal and opposite ground reaction force is akin to literally putting the 'brakes' on as a runner. This is why such ground reaction forces are often referred to as 'braking forces'.

When a runner overstrides and encounters equal and opposite ground reaction forces with each stride (see following figure), the runner must exert extra energy to overcome the braking forces. The runner's body has to get 'up and over' the foot as it lands, which requires the body to move higher into the air following each impact in order to generate and maintain momentum. This results in the up and down bopping motion observed in the overstriding runner.

ground reaction force 2-3 x body
weight

In addition to an increased risk of injury, the other problem with excessive bopping is that it slows a runner down. The longer the runner's body spends going up and down, the less time it spends going 'along the road' in the direction it needs to go to get to the finish line. In other words, time spent going up and down comes at the cost of running speed.

In contrast, the runner who does not overstride, but has their foot at the time of impact land under their centre of mass, will not need to bop up and down in order to generate momentum. They will therefore appear to run 'smoother'.

If you watch the side view of any elite runner at the front of any race, you will observe their head position is almost parallel to the road. Their body is projected forward with minimal up and down movements. I liken elite runners' bodies to being like fixed 'boxes' from the waist up. Their torsos hardly move except for the swinging of their arms. The elite runner with great technique has legs that propel them in an almost 'cyclist-like' circular and smooth movement. These runners tend to travel horizontally instead of vertically, which makes sense given that the finish line is always forwards and not upwards!

Remember, a flat trajectory is more economical than a trajectory of bopping up and down.

Reducing excessive bopping

The good news is that if you focus on correcting overstriding by running with a cadence of 90 steps/min, you will eliminate the majority of excess bopping. This occurs because a runner taking shorter and quicker steps experiences a smoother body trajectory with less up and down movement.

Running with a cadence of 90 single steps/min negates the excessive braking forces that an overstriding runner experiences. At this cadence the foot lands under the knee close to the body's centre of mass, and the braking forces of an overstriding runner are no longer experienced. However, the friction or resistance from the ground will still need to be overcome.

In addition to running with a cadence of 90 steps/min, other tips to ensure you run smoothly with minimal bopping up and down include the following:

> Recite a mantra such as 'I run light, smooth, fast and easy' as you run. By reinforcing this message your body is more likely to run in the way it is being instructed – 'light, smooth, fast and easy'!

> When going for a run, take note of the sensation of where your energy is going. Is it going up and down? Or is it

being projected forwards smoothly down the road towards the finish line?

> Have a running buddy video your running motion. You do not need elaborate equipment – simply use your smartphone or digital camera to capture 30 seconds of side-on running footage. This will allow you to analyse the degree of bopping of your body. Capturing this footage while you run on a treadmill, with ideally a plain white wall in the background, is best. Many great smartphone apps (such as Ubersense and Coach My Video) are now available that help you to capture running footage and then review it in slow motion.

It's worth noting that when a runner's technique is analysed in slow motion, a relatively large degree of bopping up and down will often appear. This is due to the exaggerated movements that slow motion analysis produces. But when running at normal pace, the bopping up and down of a proficient runner with great technique will be negligible.

Principle 3: Optimise foot placement

The third principle of great running technique is to ensure that the correct part of a runner's foot comes into contact with the ground at the time of impact.

The foot is an amazing and complex structure. Twenty-six bones (one-quarter of the total number of bones in a human body), 33 joints, and more than 100 muscles, tendons and ligaments are found in the human foot.

The foot has three regions: the forefoot, which contains the metatarsal and phalange (toe) bones; the rear-foot, which contains two of the seven tarsal bones; and the mid-foot, which contains the remaining five tarsal bones. The mid-foot, as the name suggests, is the middle of the foot between the forefoot (toes) and rear-foot (heel). See the diagram below to locate these three regions.

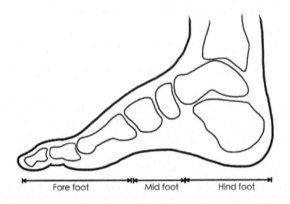

Fore foot   Mid foot   Hind foot

In order to best maximise the likelihood of running pain and injury free (as well as faster), a runner's foot at the time of impact I believe should ideally make contact at the mid-foot or forefoot. As with minimising excessive bopping motion (principle 2), running with a correct cadence of 90 single steps/min is the best way to achieve such optimal foot placement on foot landing.

However, when it comes to scientific research, the theory that forefoot or mid-foot strikers are less likely to get injured compared with their heel striking counterparts is debatable. Many would argue that research and data is insufficient to conclusively prove that heel striking increases injury risk. Surprisingly, very few studies have actually looked at the difference in injury rates between forefoot, mid-foot, and heel striking runners.

In terms of a reduced injury risk, however, several studies have yielded results that favour forefoot or mid-foot strike patterns over heel striking. One study found that runners who habitually land on their heel (rear-foot strike) incurred a greater degree of repetitive stress injuries (such as shin splints) compared with runners who mostly landed on the front of their foot (fore-foot).[13] Similarly, a 2012 study of Division 1 cross country runners found heel strikers had twice the rate of injuries when compared with mid-foot and forefoot strikers.[14]

Landing with a concurrent mid-foot and heel contact is in my opinion also a preferred foot placement as opposed to a heel strike. This concurrent foot strike, where the heel lands concurrently with the forefoot, is one of the hallmark teachings of the Chi Running technique method. Chi runners are instructed to aim for a 'flat foot' on foot contact, whereby the forefoot and rear-foot make ground contact simultaneously.

Problems occur when a runner lands repeatedly on their heels – which is what happens with overstriding. When the heels are the first point of contact, the runner's natural 'shock absorbers' are bypassed, and they encounter ground reaction forces that travel up the leg. In this instance, striking the ground with a stiff leg also requires extra energy output at every stride to overcome the 'braking force' that the ground exerts on the runner's body.

On impact, the bones of the foot and supporting soft tissues move in concert to dissipate and lessen the loads encountered upon landing. The plantar fascia softens and the foot joints 'splay' in order to minimise the load that the foot encounters on landing and impact. The foot splaying in turn minimises the load that is passed up the body to other structures such as the Achilles tendon, claves, knees, hamstrings, quadriceps, hip and, ultimately, the lower back.

In contrast to the mid-foot, the heel doesn't have any of these load-minimising or shock absorptive features, rather it is comprised of just the heel bone and a thin layer of over-lying skin. The overstriding and heel-striking runner dangerously bypasses the foot's 'built-in' shock absorbers such as the plantar fasciitis and mid-foot joints as described. Because they're not using these natural shock absorbers, these runners go on to run slower and with a much higher injury risk.

In order to optimise your foot placement try the following:

> Ensure your running cadence is 90 single steps/min.

> Practise the following drill: bounce on your heels ten times (this feels horrible and unco-ordinated), bounce on your tippy toes ten times (very fatiguing), and then bounce in-between these two extremes (that is, between the tips of your toes and the heel). What you are landing on here is the mid-foot, and this is the preferred foot contact position for runners. Visit www.pogophysio.com.au/book-resources to watch this drill in action (Optimising foot placement drill).

If you are not yet convinced of the perils of failing to optimise your foot placement on landing, I suggest you take a hammer and repeatedly bang it on your heel bone. Absurd, yes, but let me explain. If you ran an average of 30 kilometres a week for one year, this would be equivalent to 1.5 million heel-strikes or hammer blows. Ouch! It is little wonder that runners who do not optimise their foot placement get injured. The take-home message is simple: where possible avoid heel striking. The heel is merely covered by skin and is not designed to be a shock-absorbing anatomical structure.

It should also be noted that when it comes to optimal foot placement when running, even some of the fastest runners still land heel first. In fact, when the top 20 American male and female 10-kilometre track runners were analysed with high definition video analysis at the US 2012 Olympic trials, four of the top 20 men, and five of the top 20 women were found to heel-strike on landing. This showcases that even at the elite level, foot strike placement may vary. It also proves that you can still run fast even with a heel-strike. However, if I am coaching an injured runner on how to best get back from injury, or a runner who is keen to avoid injury, I will always recommend a forefoot or mid-foot landing over a heel-strike landing.

Principle 4: Optimise your body position

In addition to the three technique principles covered so far, many runners also lack awareness of their body position when running. The positioning of a runner's body can be a major hindrance to a runner's quest to run pain and injury free, and faster. The good news is that for those runners who do position their body well, they are able to tap into 'free speed' and enjoy a reduced injury risk.

As already noted, when a runner overstrides their foot lands out in front of their body. On impact, the body's resultant position is one that is leaning backwards. The leg on impact is extended straight and the runner's torso, from the waist up, is on a backwards lean (refer to the previous illustration).

One obvious problem with leaning backwards is that the runner is leaning away from the very direction they need to go! Clearly this makes no sense and is counterproductive to the runner's aim of running as fast as possible.

In contrast, leaning 'into' your run (i.e. leaning forward from the ankles) allows gravity to pull you forwards, reducing the workload of the legs. It makes sense to move from point A to point B by allowing gravity to 'pull' you there, as opposed to 'pushing' yourself there. Forward lean is analogous to the accelerator in your car; if you want to go faster, lean in more – put your foot on the accelerator. If you want to run slower, simply lean back and take your foot off the accelerator.

In addition to slower running speeds, the other problem with a backwards body lean is that the body must deal with the injury-creating braking forces that are encountered with foot strike impact. These forces are the same braking forces that the overstriding runner encounters.

The alternative is to run with the body positioned well. A good body position for a runner is characterised by the following:

> Forward lean that occurs from the ankles (not the waist). The angle of forwards lean is approximately 10 to 15 degrees.

> The head is looking ahead at the horizon and not down. Looking down tends to make the runner bend at the waist and 'fold' into the ground.

> The chest is projecting forwards and upwards from the sternum. This creates a 'lift' effect for the runner's torso and hips.

> The runner's bottom is 'tucked under'. Many runners run like they are sitting in a chair with the bottom in effect 'sticking out'. This is often due to tight hip flexors and quadriceps, which can be the result of prolonged sitting. Simply tucking the bottom or tail bone 'under' while running can create a taller runner with better technique and, therefore, efficiency. Stretching the hip flexors and quadriceps is also useful.

In order to optimise your body position, try the following when running:

> Project your body upwards – don't look down to the ground. If you look down to the ground, your body will follow your head position – down! Instead, look straight ahead and project your sternum (breastbone) upwards on an angle of about 45 degrees to the ground. If you feel confident when you run, you will look confident, and a confident runner is a fast runner!

> Use your arms. Runners regularly ask me about what to do with their arms when they run. Most of the runner's attention is directed to what their legs are doing. Yet the

145

arms play an important role in setting a good rhythm and leg cadence and propulsion.

You can ensure that your arms are contributing toward running with good technique in several key ways. They are:

» Keep your shoulders relaxed and away from your ears. I often joke with runners to not let their 'shoulders eat their ears'.

» Minimise excessive movements of the arms. You need some arm movement as a runner because this allows for rotational stability of your body. A runner who tries to minimise their arm movements will not benefit from the stability that good arm rhythm and swing can produce.

» Keep the angle at your forearm to upper arm close to 90 degrees.

» Don't let your hands cross the midline of your body.

» Move your arms faster if you want your legs to follow. When running on the flat, arms help to generate forward propulsion. When running uphill, the arms generate even greater propulsion.

» Make sure your hands come back as far as your hip. Imagine you are 'elbowing' someone behind you with the tip of your elbow.

» Don't allow your hands to drop below your waistline. This wastes energy as it is easier to swing a short arm lever compared with a long arm lever.

» Keep the fists gently clenched with the thumb resting on top. Many runners make the mistake of generating too much pressure through their hands when they run. This will only serve to tense the entire upper body, which will have a negative effect on running economy. A good and fun drill to practise in order to learn to not generate excessive hand tension is placing a dry leave between the first and second fingers when you run. You should then aim to finish the run without having crushed the dry leaf: if the leaf is crushed it indicates that too much tension was generated when running through the hands.

> Practise the 'Michael Jackson' drill. This is one of the best methods I use to teach runners about body position and forwards lean – go to www.pogophysio.com.au/book-resources to view this drill (Optimising your body position). The drill can quickly educate you about the 'free energy' that can be gained by leaning forwards rather than backwards. Many runners will never experience this free energy because they will continue to lean backwards – don't be one of them. As you practise this drill, take note of the sensation of how it feels to have your body pulled forwards by gravity, and what it feels like to hold your body straight as you fall forwards. As you practise the drill, it is important to keep your body straight and your ankles relaxed. If you are relaxing your ankles, your heels will not lift off the ground, and you won't feel any pressure increase on the balls of your feet.

Principle 5: Utilise your natural springs

The fifth principle to running with great technique is to utilise what I refer to as a runner's 'natural springs'. The same anatomical foot and leg structures that assist in lessening the loads on the legs on impact, such as the muscles, tendons and fascia, also assist with propulsion.

So when a runner overstrides and subsequently heel-strikes, not only are they bypassing their own shock absorbers they are also in effect bypassing their body's very own natural springs. The natural springs are the tendon-related structures in the foot and lower leg, including the Achilles tendon, calf muscle complex, and plantar fascia of the foot. When a runner lands on their mid- or forefoot, these natural spring structures generate energy and propulsion as they are stretched and then 'released'.

Think of how a rubber band behaves when stretched. It stretches first before it then 'snaps' or recoils back to its original length. The rubber band releases energy as it 'snaps back'. This principle in biomechanics is known as 'elastic recoil'.

Elastic recoil applies to the tendons of the human body in the same way that it applies to a rubber band. The same energy that is created by a rubber band recoiling is also generated by the plantar fascia of a runner's feet, the Achilles tendon, and the tendons in the calf complex. This occurs when a runner impacts the ground, the tendons stretch as they absorb load, before they recoil and provide the runner with propulsion.

In order to appreciate the principle of elastic recoil at work, Peter MacGill (author of *Build Your Running Body*) suggests that you tap your index finger on your thigh as hard as you can. Go on, try it! Now take your other hand and pull your index finger back as far as it will go before releasing it. I'm sure your finger on this hand hit your thigh much harder than the muscle-only generated thigh tapping. This is due to the elastic recoil and energy stored in the finger that was bent backwards before it was released to 'slam' into the thigh.

Structurally, tendons can undergo stretching or deformation of somewhere between 4 and 6 per cent of their original length. When at rest, the tendon fibres, called collagen, run parallel in wavy lines (think of rolling hills in the country-side). Under load (such as at the time of foot impact), the collagen fibres are aligned as they straighten and store energy. As the lower limb muscles contract the tendons then release their stored up energy. Amazingly, the recoil generated by a runner's leg tendons under the weight bearing or 'stance' phase of the gait cycle provides up to 50 per cent of the propulsive forces required for each stride.[15]

This elastic energy is released as kinetic (movement producing) energy during the 'toe off' part of the running cycle. Elastic recoil requires very little energy, and the good news is that it is available for us to use as runners – unless, of course, we bypass these springs by overstriding or running with less than an ideal technique.

When a runner overstrides, they inadvertently rob themselves of this free propulsive energy. Efficient runners store energy from one stride to the next and release it for push off. If it appears as though these runners have springs in their shoes, it is because they actually do!

What body frames tell us about tendons

The role that our tendons play in efficient and sustained distance running is evidenced by the body frames of elite distance runners. Typically, an elite distance runner's frame is composed of very little muscle mass, leaving just bones and tendons as the main propulsive structures. The fact that such a large proportion of their body mass is tendon tissue highlights the importance of tendons in fast and economical running.

When we compare the body shape of the distance runner to that of a sprinter, we can see marked differences. Notably, sprinters are very bulked up with large muscle masses. Sprinters require a large muscle mass for fast sprinting in order to generate power. While they transfer all the force produced by the muscle onto the bones that the muscle will act on, having large muscle mass overrides the effect of tendons.

Comparison of running bodies

Sprinter   Distance runner

In order to run pain and injury free, and also faster, it is also helpful to have 'stiff' tendons. Stiffer tendons are able to store more energy because greater energy is required to stretch them. This greater energy is stored in the tendons and released at toe off as the muscles of the calf and lower leg contract. To improve the elastic recoil of your lower limb tendons you need to make your tendons stiffer. This can be achieved by strengthening the fibres that make up the tendons with exercises such as single-leg calf raises. I recommend that all runners perform 30 single calf raises a day. Visit www.pogophysio.com.au/book-resources to view this exercise (Single-leg calf raises).

In order to optimise the utilisation of your natural springs, try the following:

> Do not overstride. Run with a cadence of 90 steps/min. This will ensure your foot lands on the mid- or forefoot whereby the Achilles tendon, plantar fascia, and other lower limb tendons are stretched and store up energy. This stored energy when released at toe off will give a 'free push' and 'free speed'. (Running with a cadence of 90 steps/min also minimises a runner's foot contact time. The aim of every runner should be to minimise foot contact time in order to decrease the injurious effects of greater lower limb loading rates that result from with prolonged foot contact time.)

> Practise the 'two-legged hop' drill. With feet shoulder-width apart, practise bouncing up and down very quickly, landing on the balls of the feet. Aim to bounce as quickly and lightly as you can. Bounce for 30 seconds and repeat three times. This drill teaches your body to land on the

mid-foot and to maximise the effect of running with maximum tendon utilisation. (Refer to www.pogophysio. com.au/book-resources.) This drill is best completed before the start of each training run to reinforce the use of your natural springs.

> Incorporate some 'plyometric training'. Plyometrics evolved in the early 1980s when they were used by Soviet track and field athletes. Plyometric training involves exercises where a runner or athlete moves from a muscle stretched position, to a contracted muscle position, and then back to a muscle lengthened position. Exercises such as box jumps, squat jumps, high skipping, and bounding are examples of plyometric training. Here are some examples of plyometric training you can add to your training:

  » Bounding for 60 metres. Spring off the toes as you project yourself forwards at an angle of 20 to 30 degrees. Repeat three times.

  » Sets of eight box jumps. Jump up onto a box at least 40 centimetres in height, and then back down. Try three sets with a two-minute break between sets.

  » Sets of five squat jumps. Simply squat down as far as you can and then spring forth as you explode up into the air before landing in a squat position to finish. Try three sets of good quality reps.

> Incorporate some hill sprints. The hill must be steep and short. Run ten reps of the hill with two minutes recovery

between sets. The sprint should be between 8 and 12 seconds. Aim for three sets. (See the following section for more on running hills.)

How to run hills (bonus)

In addition to the five principles of great running technique covered in this chapter, I thought it would be useful to provide some instruction on the running technique required to run hills well. Almost every runner who receives some running technique instruction wants to know how to run hills. The following tips will hopefully turn you into a runner who enjoys running hills, and a runner who runs them both looking good and with efficiency and speed:

> Relax when going up the hill, being sure to expend only marginally more energy than what you spend when running on the flat.

> On the way down, fight the tendency to 'lean back' and away from the hill and instead 'lean into it' – let yourself go. You won't face plant – I promise! This is gravity assisting you to get down the hill faster.

> Aim to keep your cadence quick and consistent (90 steps/min), just as you would when running the flat. As you run uphill, you will need to shorten your stride length, and when running downhill you will obviously take longer strides. However, do not allow your strides to lengthen to the point where your cadence starts to drop. Instead, keep your cadence consistent at 90 steps/min.

> Look up to where you are going (that is, the top of the hill) and not at your feet.

> When going downhill, hold a wider arm angle than normal in order to assist with balance of the body.

Before we move onto the third step of how to run pain and injury free, I have two closing thoughts on running with great technique.

First, don't forget that you *can* 'teach an old dog new tricks'. Some of the studies and research findings shared in this chapter highlight this. When running technique is taught, changes can result. Even the runner with years of an ingrained running style can make positive technique changes.

Second, on average, it takes runners three to six months to improve their running technique. So, remember to keep it simple. Don't try to do too much, or too many things at once. Pick one of the five outlined principles and integrate that well, before you move onto the next principle. If you try to do too much at once it is likely you will 'spin your wheels', get frustrated, and end up achieving nothing.

Yes, the process of learning how to run with great technique adds a 'cognitive load' by way of thought processes that previously you may not have had to 'worry about'. But this process is not meant to be too burdensome or mentally taxing.

Take a moment to look through the key points for this chapter, and then you are ready for step three – navigating the footwear maze.

Step 2: Run with great technique – key points

Here are the key points to remember from this chapter:

> Most runners are unaware of the role that running technique plays as a contributory factor to the development of running injuries, and as a determining factor of running speed.

> Although running occurs 'naturally', running with great technique must be practised and learned.

> You can get faster as a runner in one of three ways. Improving your running technique, elevating your lactate threshold, or by optimising your genetically determined VO2max.

> By correcting running technique, running economy can be improved. This will result in being able to sustain a faster running pace for longer.

> Five principles constitute great running technique: avoiding overstriding, minimising bopping, optimising foot placement on landing, optimising body position, and utilising your natural springs. For best results keep it simple and work on one principle at a time.

Step 2: Run with great technique – key points (continued)

> The most vital principle for running with great technique is to ensure you run with a cadence of close to 90 single steps/min. This will lessen the likelihood of you overstriding, which will in turn benefit your efforts to apply principles 2 to 5.

Case study: Ralph – the benefits of improving running technique

Ralph initially presented for physiotherapy seeking assistance with two areas of concern: his left hip and left ankle. Ralph was initially experiencing pain with basic daily activities such as sitting and going from sitting to standing. Even small runs were causing pain in both the front of the ankle, and the front of the hip. These hip and ankle pains had become a point of frustration and concern for Ralph, and Ralph was committed to achieving an outcome.

Assessment and imaging of both the ankle and the hip showed bony growths that were resulting in hip and ankle impingements.

Ralph's rehabilitation included manual (hands-on) therapy in order to reduce pain and improve the function of the hip and ankle. In combination with 'hands on' manual therapy, Ralph was prescribed a progressive home exercise program that comprised stretching, and

---

Case study: Ralph – the benefits of improving running technique (continued)

hip and ankle strengthening exercises. Ralph also reduced his body weight, which aided in de-loading the painful ankle and hip.

Given that Ralph had an ambition to progressively increase his run training, I encouraged Ralph to receive some tuition regarding his running technique. Ralph attended my RUN101 Technique Workshop and set about making technique changes. The changes were made over an eight-week period following the workshop. The greatest change Ralph made was a reduction in stride length, and an increase in cadence from 77 steps/min to 86 to 90 steps/min.

The resultant improvement in Ralph's running technique was profound. Ralph is now running three to four times per week, with his longest run in excess of 20 kilometres. The best part is that Ralph no longer suffers from the ankle or hip pain. Ralph now has ambitions to run a marathon.

Chapter 7

STEP 3: Navigate the footwear maze

Step 1: Discover your running body

Step 2: Run with great technique

Step 3: Navigate the footwear maze

Step 4: The importance of hip stability

Step 5: The power of rest

If the shoe fits …

The third step to running pain and injury free is to ensure that you have made an appropriate running shoe selection.

Getting the correct or 'perfect' running shoe is often perceived by runners to be the panacea for all of running's ills and injuries. However, before running shoes are considered you need to have gained an appreciation of the first two steps to running pain and injury free (covered in chapters 5 and 6).

Running pain and injury free starts with discovering your running body. It is fundamental to first know your genetic mobility status, running screening results, ideal frame weight, and body maintenance cycle. Being aware of what constitutes great running technique should also precede a runner focusing on footwear selection.

If the first two steps of this five step method are not applied, selecting the correct running shoe will not serve or benefit you as it should.

It has been said that how one runs is probably more important than what is on a runner's feet. However, what's on a runner's feet affects how the runner runs. As a result, if your goal is to experience pain- and injury-free running, you will need some knowledge of how to best select a suitable pair of running shoes.

In clinical practice, I educate injured runners that it's best to focus on what their body is doing before they start running (step one), followed by a focus on what their body is doing once it is running (step two), before they get concerned about what running shoes they have on their feet.

Consider the following example of how knowing your running body before selecting shoes can be advantageous in then selecting shoes.

A hypermobile runner, through their running screening, discovers that they have weak hip muscles. This is evidenced by a reduced hip external rotation measurement during their running screening. The runner is then instructed to correct the hip muscle weaknesses through targeted exercise.

As a result the runner is then able to select a lighter weight running shoe because the lower limb will now be subjected to much less load as a result of the pelvis and hips being strong and stable. A lighter running shoe positively affects running technique as it provides the runner with greater foot placement feedback – which aids the runner to have the foot land more directly underneath the hip and close to the body's centre of mass. The lighter shoe lessens the likelihood of the runner overstriding, which then produces a reduced risk of lower limb injury. The other benefit of the runner discovering their running body before selecting shoes was that the lighter shoe choice made because of adequate hip stability will also now result in faster running.

Prior to the runner gaining knowledge of their running body and, in particular, their hip weakness, the runner may have encountered injury and problems if they had selected a lighter style running shoe, based on a current popular fad of running in lightweight shoes.

In clinical practice it is common for me to recommend lighter shoes for runners who have progressed through steps one and two. I can safely make such a recommendation because I know that they are addressing their body's problem areas with appropriate exercises. The net effect of these exercises is to make their bodies more robust and injury proofed. In being stronger and in 'better shape', the runner can more safely opt for a running shoe that is lower in weight and in general not as 'bulky'.

Working through the Footwear Maze

Given the enormous range of running shoes now available, choosing the best shoe for the modern-day runner is not an easy task. The running shoe market is loaded with options and an ever-increasing variety. You can get heavy shoes, light shoes, flexible shoes, solid shoes, shoes with funny toes, shoes with big heels, shoes with small heels, shoes with 'in-between' heels, shoes with rocker bottoms, shoes with porous materials, shoes with no laces – and the list could go on. In fact, over two hundred running shoe brands are now available for consumers.

Shoe categories have also expanded, and now include options such as minimalist, trail, maximum absorption, racing, high-mileage, moderate stability, mild stability, firm neutral, race trainers, and flexible neutral shoes. Such shoes are in addition to the every-day motion control shoe.

As recently as only two decades ago, three running shoe categories were generally accepted and recognised. All shoes belonged to the neutral, stability, or motion-control categories. Needless to say, two decades ago things were much simpler!

In addition to the confusion created by this extensive range of shoes and shoe categories, shoe companies produce an endless array of marketing. Such marketing typically states that the company's new shoe 'technology' is the very thing that runners have been waiting for. The marketing message is to proudly present the latest in running shoe innovations. Such innovations may be marketed as being able to control excessive motion of this foot part, and allow for maximal motion of that body part – all while suggesting that the runner can go further faster with fewer injuries.

The end result is that the running shoe consumer is left feeling confused. I observe this confusion on an almost daily basis. With so many options, all promising so much, running shoe consumers are left to wonder which shoe is best for them.

There is seldom a day in practice when I do not get asked by an injured runner which shoes they should be wearing. The injured runner will normally confide that when it comes to purchasing their running shoes, they feel at the mercy of the footwear company's marketing and claims. They characteristically feel vulnerable, uncertain, and ill equipped to navigate the footwear maze.

To the injured and non-injured runner, getting a health professional's shoe recommendation is welcomed advice. However, not all runners will have access to a trusted source such as a health professional. The runner is normally at best reliant on the knowledge of the shoe salesperson. Any information and education about how to best navigate the footwear maze will assist in better running shoe selection. This, the second step in the five-step run pain free process, will provide you with the information required to navigate the footwear maze and make an appropriate running shoe selection.

Not so fast – there's a lot to consider

In making a shoe recommendation for an injured runner, I take into account many considerations. A well-considered shoe selection should extend beyond merely matching a shoe based on a runner's basic foot type.

Over the last decade, most shoe salespersons' recommendations have been made purely on the basis of a runner's foot type. However, a runner's basic foot type, while an important consideration, is just one of numerous considerations that should influence running shoe selection.

While foot scans such as those available in retail shoe stores may be performed to analyse foot type, matching a shoe to a 'foot', instead of matching the shoe to the 'runner' is, in my opinion, far from ideal.

When making footwear selections for both injured and non-injured runners as a physiotherapist, I consider the following:

> volume of training

> consistency of training

> genetic mobility status (hypermobile or hypomobile)

> event goals

> running screening results (potential problem areas)

> injury risk factors (for example, deficiency of hip stability or quadriceps tightness)

> injury history

> current injury profile

> event preparation (time until the runner's next event)

> body weight compared to their ideal frame weight

> diligence with their body maintenance routine

> personal preferences (for brands and colours, etc.)

> feedback and experience with previous shoe selections

> use of orthotics

> current running technique and any technique flaws.

The preceding list is obviously comprehensive. While these considerations are part of my decision-making algorithm, your decision-making process does not need to be as complex.

This chapter is all about you gaining the confidence to select a running shoe with some certainty and knowledge. I want you to feel confident in your shoe selection. Please note that because of the ever-evolving shoe landscape, where new shoe models and styles are continually being released, I do not list specific brands or shoe models; however, I do refer to shoe 'categories' to help guide you.

In addition to acquiring this knowledge, it's also important to have some context about running shoes in general. Having some insight into the role running shoes play in faster running and in injury minimisation, as well as the three basic foot types, will also be of use in assisting you to navigate the footwear maze. Let's take a look.

Form before footwear

In my practice, I am often heard saying that 'magic happens' when a runner with great technique and body awareness is placed into a running shoe suitable for their body and their running needs. The result of matching the right shoe to a well-conditioned runner (their body) who is running with great technique is normally soaring levels of enjoyment, lowered injury risk and personal best running times.

Yet, as already mentioned, it is counterproductive to focus on getting the right shoe before a runner first learns and understands the importance of running with great technique. A runner who starts with addressing their running technique before attempting to make a perfect shoe choice will have a head start in their quest to run pain and injury free. By making technique changes such as shortening their stride, getting off their heels, improving their body position, and utilising the tendon springs in their legs, the runner has, in effect, taken out a degree of 'injury insurance'. These positive technique changes result in less loading on areas prone to injury such as the foot, knee, and hip joints.

Some runners incorrectly assume that correct shoe selection will 'cure all ills' and produce faster running. They fail to take into account contributory injury factors other than their shoe selection. Clever shoe marketing has conditioned runners to ignore the obvious (what they are doing with their body when running – their technique) and place all faith in the shoe doing 'everything' on their behalf.

The runner who has made, to their knowledge, a savvy and informed shoe purchase is normally confused and frustrated when a running injury develops. They are often left to ponder whether they were in fact running in the 'right shoes', and whether their injury was a direct result of wearing the wrong shoes.

Correct running shoe selection is important in a runner's quest for pain- and injury-free running. But it must be remembered that shoes cannot, and will not, be the panacea for running injury prevention. As we delve deeper into step three, remember that running technique (form) should always come before footwear selection.

The benefits of the right shoe choice

While shoe selection certainly isn't a panacea for preventing all running injuries, it does have clear benefits, covered in the following sections.

Shoe choice can aid faster running

Making an appropriate shoe choice can result in faster running. A well-selected pair of running shoes will aid with faster running through:

1   *Weighing less.* The logic is very simple. Heavier shoes require the legs to do extra work, which will slow the runner down. While a runner must have the required comfort and support, I routinely observe runners training in shoes that are heavier than they need to be.

For example, a typical stability training shoe may weigh 200 to 300 grams per shoe. Contrast this to a lighter shoe that is equally as suitable for the runner, which may weigh 150 to 250 grams less. To put this in perspective, the lighter shoes' weight would be less than the weight of an Apple iPad. Yes that's light!

The extra weight of a heavier shoe may not seem like a lot but it quickly adds up. Especially when you consider that for one hour of running each leg will likely do 5,400 repetitions (60 minutes × 90 steps/min). The lightness of the shoe helps facilitate quick leg turnover, which avoids the pitfall of overstriding and the resultant perilous heel-strike discussed in chapter 3.

According to US-based running coach Jack Daniels, a runner will expend 1 per cent more aerobic energy for every 100 grams that a shoe weighs, with a reduction in shoe weight of 100 grams shaving 0.83 seconds off each mile of running. Extrapolate this over a marathon and even a 100-gram reduction on shoe weight may shave 3 minutes off a marathon time! In fact, researchers have recently confirmed that every 100 grams of extra shoe weight creates a 1 per cent increase in oxygen consumption.[1] This can be significant for the runner who is aiming to get the most out of their performance.

2   *Assisting you with staying injury free.* A well-selected pair of shoes, while not an injury panacea, can bolster your body's defences against developing a running injury. An example is the runner experiencing ongoing calf or Achilles problems. Such a runner would find benefit in running in a shoe that has a slightly higher heel as opposed to a flatter more minimalistic running shoe. The greater heel height can de-load the Achilles tendon and calf muscles. Being injury free will then allow for consistent and uninterrupted training. With this consistency of training will come bettered performance and a greater enjoyment of running.

3   *Improving your confidence.* Knowing that you are running in a well-selected pair of shoes will boost confidence levels. Every athlete performs better when they feel confident about their 'equipment'. In a runner's case, their equipment is their shoes! In practice, I have observed the heightened confidence that a runner has when they make a shoe purchase decision based on the information shared in this chapter.

In addition to aiding performance, the correct shoe selection will also benefit the runner by way of minimising the onset of running-related injuries. The next section describes how.

Shoe choice can aid injury prevention

Selecting an appropriate pair of running shoes can also reduce the risk of an injury developing. A well-selected pair of running shoes will aid with injury prevention by:

1 *Weighing less.* A lighter shoe will result in improved running technique through helping the runner minimise overstriding, maximise cadence, and optimise foot placement on landing. If you run with great technique, you can often go for a lighter and less bulky shoe. However be mindful that lighter isn't always better when it comes to selecting your running shoes and injury risk reduction.

   For example, one study found that runners who ran in a Nike Free 3.0 shoe for 12 weeks incurred more injuries than those who ran in the heavier Nike Pegasus shoe.[2] It should be noted that this same study also reported that runners who ran in Vibram shoes (ultra-light shoes) were found to suffer fewer injuries than the heavier Nike Free 3.0 shoes. These results are interesting in that you can extrapolate (from the findings) and say that lighter shoes were superior to heavy shoes in reducing injuries, or vice versa. One possible reason for the same study reporting such mixed results is that injury prevention extends beyond running in lighter weight shoes, and includes other possible causes such as running technique, and the musculoskeletal health of the runner, variables not analysed in the aforementioned study.

2   *De-loading key structures that may be injured or painful.*
A runner who is suffering from Achilles tendon problems
(or has in the past) may, for example, assist their
rehabilitation by running in a shoe with a moderate heel
height. The raising of the heel will help to reduce the
tension the painful tendon experiences, effectively 'de-
loading' the Achilles tendon.

This same principle of selecting a shoe with a more
raised heel also applies for a runner who is suffering from
forefoot pain. Forefoot pain may include conditions such
as metatarsalgia (pain of the long toe bones), or inter-
metatarsal bursitis (inflammation of the 'shock absorbers')
between toe bones (metatarsals), or osteoarthritis of the
mid-foot or forefoot joints.

A further example of footwear selection aiding in
reducing running injuries includes the runner suffering
from ongoing knee pain. In this example, the runner may
benefit from transitioning from a heavier pair of shoes
into a lighter pair of shoes. The lighter shoes allow for a
shorter stride length and quicker cadence, which has the
effect of reducing adverse pressures or loads on the
knee joint.

3   *Reducing unwanted loading and movements of the hip
and knee joints.* Researchers found that running barefoot
reduced adverse 'collapsing' movements (adduction and
internal rotation) at the hip joint.[3] This was thought to
be a function of the change in running technique elicited
through changes in cadence and reductions in hip and

knee joint loading. Researchers proposed that these technique changes and decreases in joint loading were brought about by the removal of normal motion control running shoes. In interpreting these research findings, one could reason that if barefoot running had a positive effect on injury minimising movements, running in lightweight shoes would likely produce similar effects.

Once again, though, it needs to be stated that no running shoe on its own can be viewed as being a panacea for all running injuries! As runners we are all built differently. A pair of shoes that may help one injured runner overcome their injury may be injurious to another.

Keeping the information shared so far in this chapter in mind – and before exploring the key principles of footwear selection – we need to take a look at foot types, a thing called 'pronation', orthotics, and a little on the history and evolution of running shoes. Having some background and fundamental knowledge about these topics is important because it serves as the basis for today's busy shoe landscape.

The three foot types and how to tell which you are

To date, research has not validated the prescription of running shoes based on a runner's foot type. However, I believe that having some knowledge of your foot type is still of some use in running shoe selection, primarily because it gives you an insight into your genetic mobility status. Foot type is characteristically determined by a runner's arch height. For example, if you have a flat foot or a low arch height, you will likely be a hypermobile runner. This is a function of the more elastic connective tissues in the foot, which result in greater deformation (collapsing of the tissues toward the ground) under the body weight of the hypermobile runner. While I am not aware of any research or studies that link hypermobility to arch height, I have made this observation over my years in clinical practice. Naturally, there are exceptions to this observation and variations will occur. For example you may get a hypermobile runner who exhibits a neutral arch. Rarely, though, would you see a hypermobile runner with a high arch foot.

In contrast, hypomobile runners' feet tend to be 'high arched' or in between a high and low arch. We refer to such in-between arches as being 'neutral'.

With this in mind, I tend to categorise feet into three basic foot types. These are shown in the following table and figure.

Foot type	Low-arch foot	High-arch foot	Normal foot
Approximate % of population exhibiting foot type	67%	3%	30%
Also known as	Over-pronated foot	Supinated foot	Neutral

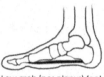 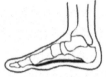 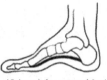

Low arch (pes planus) foot   Normal arch(neutral) foot   High arch (pes cavus) foot

Working out your basic foot type

You can take several tests at home to determine your basic foot type. The tests are as follows:

1   *The 'wet foot' test.* Stand in a tub of water and then step out onto some heavy butcher's paper. Take note of which of the three basic foot types you are. See the following illustration for interpretation.

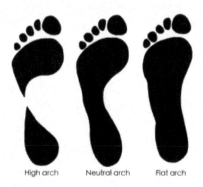

High arch   Neutral arch   Flat arch

For many years (from the late 80s and through the 90s), this test, and variations of it, were used for the fitting of running shoes. The prescription of a running shoe was based on the runner's foot type. For example, a high-arched runner would typically be fitted with a cushioned shoe. Meanwhile, a low-arched runner would routinely be prescribed a motion control shoe and the neutral runner prescribed either, or a low cushion and low stability shoe. In more modern times, use of this test for shoe prescription has largely fallen out of vogue, with current shoe prescription guidelines focusing more on comfort and 3D motion analysis and testing (more on this later in the chapter).

2   *The 'two-finger' test.* Stand at rest with your feet shoulder-width apart. See if someone can easily place their first two fingers under your arch at the level of the navicular. (The navicular is halfway along the arch.) If two 'buddied together' fingers can be placed under the navicular with clearance, you have either a neutral or high-arched foot. If the fingers do not slip under, it's likely that you have a low-arched foot (see the following illustration).

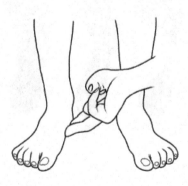

As an alternative to using these home tests to discover your foot type, consider getting a health professional such as a physiotherapist or podiatrist to provide a professional assessment. Check that your selected health professional utilises 3D gait scanning technology, which is more accurate than the preceding 'do it yourself' tests. However, in the absence of engaging a health professional, the preceding tests will equip you with some basic knowledge of your foot type.

There's more to it than foot type

In 2009, the *British Journal of Sports Medicine* published a scientific systematic review that concluded that the prescription of shoes with elevated and cushioned heels and pronation control systems based on a runner's foot type was not evidence based.[4] That is, there was insufficient data to support the prescription of shoes based on a runner's foot type, or arch height. So it should be noted that selecting a running shoe based on your foot type as described in this section is not the 'gold-standard' shoe selection strategy. While it may be commonly performed by retail shoe salespeople, this does not necessarily mean that it is the best way, or even the right way to prescribe and purchase running shoes.

In my opinion, fitting or selecting running shoes entirely based on a runner's foot type is potentially dangerous. The runner's whole body, their running technique, and all of the previously mentioned footwear considerations, should be taken into account before a running shoe is prescribed. It's critical to fit the running shoe to the runner and not just to the runner's foot.

What is pronation?

Most runners are familiar with the term 'pronation'. But what does it actually mean and is it relevant when it comes to selecting running shoes? Let's take a look.

Pronation refers to the rolling motion that the foot makes when it comes into contact with the ground. The foot must pronate in order to move through its normal range of motion. The purpose of pronation is to allow the joints and tissues of the foot to absorb and dissipate impact forces that the foot encounters when it makes ground contact. These impact forces are then transferred up the kinetic chain through the ankles, shins, knees, hips, lower back, and the body.

Of chief importance is the amount of pronation that occurs. Pronation can be quantified as either being mild, moderate, or severe. The 'rate' of foot pronation is also of importance. The rate of pronation refers to the 'speed' at which the foot rolls in. At the mild end of the pronation spectrum, the runner's foot may roll in only a small amount, and in a relatively controlled manner (slow rate). In contrast, at the severe end of pronation, the runner's foot may roll in very quickly and by a large amount (fast rate).

Pronation can be contributory to injury if there is too much of it or it occurs too quickly. In my practice, I refer to such injury contributing pronation as being 'pathological' pronation. That is the amount of pronation or the rate of pronation (or both) can contribute towards injury development or injury propagation for runners.

Let's take a look at how excessive pronation affects the body.

Understanding the effect of excessive pronation on the body

To discover the effect of excessive pronation on your body, try the following exercise:

1   Stand and pronate your feet (roll them in). What happens to your pelvis? Notice how collapsing your arch makes the knees and hips rotate inwards, and your pelvis drop forwards from the top down.

2   Now supinate your feet (roll them out). What happens to your pelvis? Notice how as your arch lifts, your knees also 'lift' and rotate slightly outwards, and your pelvis drops backwards from the top down.

3   Now flex (or drop) your pelvis. What happens to your feet? Dropping your pelvis will make your feet pronate.

4   Now extend your pelvis. What happens to your feet? Extending your pelvis will make your feet lift 'up' with an arch.

This simple exercise gives you an appreciation of how foot pronation can alter the rest of the running body.

The war on pronation

Over the years pronation has been portrayed as an enemy of runners, and much of this negative context and poor pronation 'PR' has been generated by shoe manufactures. Between the late 1980s and early 2000s, shoe manufacturers centred a lot of their shoe marketing messages on the need to prevent pronation in order to decrease injury risk. Emerging research at the time pointed to a link between pronation and lower limb common running injuries such as plantar fasciitis and shin splints.[5,6] One research finding led to another in exploring the proposed relationship between pronation and injuries, and before long it seemed like the entire running world was out to prevent 'pronation'.

What the shoe manufacturers and, indeed, the running world forgot during this time is that pronation was not 'bad'. It was forgotten that if the foot did not pronate, it would strike the ground as a rigid obstacle on the end of the leg, with such rigidity at foot impact likely to be disastrous for any runner's ambition to run without pain or injury. Rather than the impact forces a runner experiences being absorbed by the foot's joints and soft tissues when the foot pronates, the impact forces on landing would be transmitted up the leg to the Achilles tendon, calves, knees, hips, and lower back. This would likely lead to an increased risk of lower limb injuries due to the overloading of these structures. Hence, as runners we all need to have feet that pronate – if we didn't, we would quickly find ourselves in trouble!

Pronation and shoe selection

So, what has pronation got to do with shoe selection? Since the early 1980s, the major running shoe manufacturers have included anti-pronation features in the design of their shoes. Such features include stiff heel cups (or counters) at the rear of the shoe, bulky and well-supported arches, stiff midsoles, stiffer cushioning, and a multitude of proprietary technologies.

For many years, researchers and clinicians believed that anti-pronation features in shoes (and orthotics) assisted with the lowering of impact forces that a runner's body would encounter. The belief among researchers and shoe manufacturers alike was that anti-pronation shoe features actually re-aligned the runner's lower limbs. They proposed that anti-pronation shoes would stop the resultant 'rolling in' and collapsing of the knee and hip, thereby altering the runner's physical body and the runner's structural alignment.

In 2001, Canadian academic Benno Nigg proposed a new way of thinking about the role that anti-pronation shoes played in reducing running injuries.[7] Nigg refuted that anti-pronation shoes changed a runner's structural alignment, and instead he postulated that anti-pronation shoes (and also orthotics) actually resulted in changes to muscle tuning and muscle activation. That is, he proposed that the changes in muscles in being used and their pattern of use subsequently reduced impact forces associated with over-pronation, and resulted in a more normalised joint movement pattern during ground contact. Years later at the time of this book being written, Nigg's paradigm remains the most commonly accepted rationale for how orthotics and anti-pronation shoes actually effect change on a runner's body. However, there is still far from consensus in the scientific world around Nigg's paradigm.

Research findings suggest that the mechanisms of injury development and injury treatment through the control of pronation with anti-pronation shoes are not well understood. I believe that the lack of consensus in the scientific literature points back to the fact that controlling pronation only addresses one factor of what is normally an array of running injury contributory factors (see chapter 2). Despite the lack of scientific consensus around anti-pronation shoes, I maintain that if a runner over-pronates and it is contributory to the onset of a running injury, this may in part be remedied by the selection of an appropriate running shoe. An appropriate running shoe may help to slow down and control some of the excessive pronation.

The role of orthotics in controlling pronation

Sometimes if a runner's degree of pronation is excessive, in addition to a well-selected shoe, an orthotic may be required or prescribed by a health professional. An orthotic is a device that may be custom-made or pre-fabricated. Orthotics can be made from rigid (such as carbon), semi-rigid (thermoplastic), or soft (foam) materials.

The orthotic is fitted into a runner's shoes. The orthotic will normally (but not always) span the length of the foot and feature an elevated arch design. This elevated arch is designed to control either the excessive rate or amount of pronation of the runner's foot. See the following illustration for an example of an orthotic.

Runners who require orthotic support in their shoes are often the hypermobile and severely over-pronating runners. Left uncorrected, their over-pronation may represent a major injury risk factor. When an injury does develop, the over-pronation has in effect become 'pathological'. In such cases, the orthotic works to support the arch of the foot in reducing the 'rolling in' motion of the foot while running, via the effect on the activation, tuning, and patterning of the lower limb muscles as Nigg proposed.[8]

Over-pronation can also be the result (or part result) of muscular weakness and poor activation of key muscles further up the runner's kinetic chain (or body). For example, if a runner's hips collapse at the time of impact with the ground, this hip dropping can exacerbate the degree of a runner's foot pronation.

In my practice, I refer to this effect on the degree of pronation as being a deficit in 'hip stability'. This is predominantly due to weakness of the hip muscles but can also be accentuated if a runner has a hypermobile genetic mobility status. In the fourth step to running pain and injury free – chapter 8 – I cover hip stability and outline how to assess and rectify hip stability deficits.

In such cases, I tend to address hip stability before I prescribe orthotic support. Often times, when the runner stabilises their hips by way of prescribed hip strengthening exercises, the degree of their foot pronation decreases. This may then eliminate the need for an orthotic, or at a minimum modify the orthotic prescription.

A final note on orthotics

Many barefoot running purists advocate that wearing orthotics is unnecessary. Their view is an extension of their belief that running shoes in general hinder rather than help a runner in their quest to run without injury. In my clinical opinion, dismissing orthotics as being redundant can be misguided. Taking this view can be problematic because it ignores the very real and legitimate need that some runners have for orthotics, in order for them to be able to run pain and injury free.

The history of running shoes

It is believed that humans may have worn footwear such as sandals for the past 50,000 years. It is also believed that humans may have, over time, gradually adapted to wearing footwear.[9] However, significant changes to footwear occurred around the time of the first running boom.

To better understand the current running shoe landscape, having a basic appreciation of the history of running shoes helps. In this section, I break the history of running shoes down into three categories: the early years, the motion control years, and the minimalist movement (years).

The early years: 1940–1970s

Running shoes in this era were very simple. They were characteristically flat with no built-up heel, enclosed with a basic and single material upper (often canvas). They certainly did not exhibit any of the shoe features we see characterising the running shoes of today. Because of their simple design these early running shoes weighed less than the motion control shoes that followed them in the evolution of running shoe design.

If you look at images of runners competing during this era, you will observe that the running shoes look very much like a basic tennis shoe (think Dunlop Volleys). Historical photos of Australia's legendary middle distance runners such as Herb Elliot, John Landy, and Ron Clarke all showcase the use of such tennis-like running shoes. The shoes comprised of just a sole with an upper – they were designed to merely cover the feet. They were not designed or worn with the intention of reducing injuries through shock absorptive or pronation controlling features, as are the modern-day running shoes.

Looking back at the history of distance running, there is evidence of runners successfully competing in very basic running shoes void of any of the modern-day shoe technologies familiar to us today. The four-minute mile was broken by Roger Bannister, who wore nothing more than a very basic flat-soled shoe. Or take Abebe Bikila's victory in the 1960 Olympic Marathon, through the streets of Rome while running barefoot. Legend has it that the shoes Abebe had been issued were ill-fitting and at the last minute he decided to race barefoot, the way he had trained. Four years later at the 1964 Tokyo Olympic Games, Abebe defended his marathon title, becoming the first marathon defending champion in Olympic history. By this stage, Abebe had picked up a shoe sponsor (Puma) and he defended his title running in very lightweight and basic Puma shoes.

The early years of running shoes preceded what was to emerge in the 1970s with the advent of the world's first running boom – the motion control shoe.

The motion control years: 1970s–1990s

This era of running shoes coincided with the US running boom of the 1970s and 1980s. As masses of people discovered the joys of running, shoe sales soared, and manufacturers raced to meet the market's demand. Many of the manufacturers that sprang to prominence in this era are the shoe 'giants' that we are familiar with today, including Nike, Adidas, Puma, and ASICS.

The increase in participation during this era produced a proportionate increase in the number of running injuries. Opportunistically, the shoe manufacturers sought to curb the increase in injuries by the development of running shoes that controlled the 'motion' of the runner's foot. This era birthed the 'motion control' shoe, or what we now term the 'modern' running shoe.

The first motion control shoe was released in 1972 by Nike. It was known as the Nike *Cortez*. Nike was founded by Phil Knight and Bill Bowerman – Knight was a former University of Oregon runner, and Bowerman was the University of Oregon's distance running coach. There was no modern running shoe before their union.

Bowerman believed that by sticking rubber on the heel of your running shoes, a runner would be able to step ahead of their centre of gravity by way of being able to take bigger strides. This Bowerman believed would confer a performance advantage. Given what we have already covered in chapter 6 about overstriding, we know that Bowerman's belief was in fact contrary to better running performance.

However, Bowerman's famed tinkering to produce shoes in his basement using his wife's waffle maker was a raging success. The burgeoning running shoe market exploded on the back of the mass of people taking to running during the first running boom.

The motion control shoe

Motion control shoes featured various components that were designed (and marketed) to assist runners to run with less injury risk. Such components of the shoes included: elevated and cushioned heels, supportive heel counters, anti-pronation wedges, various instep sole densities, and a wide range of upper materials that provided 'stiffness', comfort, and support.

See the following figure for an example of a motion control running shoe and its components.

Stiff shoe upper

Supportive heel counter

Elevated and cushioned heel

Anti-pronation wedge

The majority of running footwear available today remains characterised by motion control shoe components. Today almost every major shoe brand has a series of motion control shoes available in the brand's range. Motion control shoes are typically stiff, and are not easily bent or flexed.

The case against motion control shoes

Barefoot and minimalist running advocates often argue against the use of motion control shoes for runners. To support their view it is interesting to note that scientific critical reviews conclude that no evidence exists to support the prescription of a motion control that has an elevated cushioned heel and pronation control system.

Tam et al reported that:

> The lack of evidence for shoe prescription and the persistently elevated presence of running injuries have been proposed as evidence that shoe technologies are ineffective, and with a somewhat large leap in logic, that barefoot running would provide the effective and viable alternative.[10]

I agree with Tam et al's sentiment that it is a tenuous hypothesis that correlates the still high incidence of running injuries with the seeming ineffectiveness of motion control running shoes. The apparent failure of modern motion control shoes to decrease the high modern injury incidence rate may in fact be due to other factors such as the greater participation of runners who have characteristics more prone to injury. Such characteristics include surplus frame weights with the uptake of recreational runners as part of the second running boom. The characteristics of modern-day fun runners' bodies are very different to those who lined up for fun runs pre-1972. My observation is that with the world's second running boom and the mass increase in running participation levels, the average marathoner today is less trained and running with greater body weight compared with the marathoner of previous generations. Therefore, if the overall injury incidence rate has remained relatively unchanged, this may in fact support the use of motion control shoes. If motion control shoes were not available, I believe that injury rates among modern-day runners would be even higher.

The minimalist movement: mid-1990s–current

Over the last two decades, the running footwear landscape has changed enormously. The changes have been largely driven by the proposed benefits of running barefoot or, alternately, running in lightweight or 'minimalist' type shoes.

Understanding the attraction of barefoot and minimalist running

The 'barefoot and minimalist' running movement emerged in the mid-1990s and has continued to grow over the last decade, following the release of Christopher McDougall's best-selling book *Born to Run* in 2009. *Born to Run* and its barefoot ideologies became so popular that they gave birth to a counter-cultural movement of runners seeking to get back to 'natural running' the 'barefoot' way. These runners began exploring and integrating barefoot running practices into their run training. Runners were rejecting the comfort of their standard and traditional motion control running shoes in favour of lightweight minimalist running shoes. Many were even attempting to go entirely barefoot.

Why were so many runners abandoning the familiar for this unknown and largely unheralded way of running? As the trend emerged, barefoot running advocates validated their approach by citing that modern-day injury rates had not decreased with the advent of the modern-day running shoe. Because the injury rates had not decreased, as previously outlined, barefoot advocates were quick to render all modern-day running shoes as ineffective and inadequate.

At the fore of the criticism of the modern-day running shoe was Dr Daniel Lieberman, a professor of biological anthropology at Harvard University. Lieberman claimed that:

> A lot of foot and knee injuries that are currently plaguing runners are actually caused by people running with shoes that make our feet weak, cause us to over-pronate, and give us knee problems. Until 1972, when the modern athletic shoe was invented by Nike, people ran in very thin soled shoes, had strong feet, and had much lower incidence of knee injuries.

As one observer of the trend of barefoot and minimalist running stated, it is with a 'rather large leap in logic' that barefoot running would provide the effective and viable alternative to traditional motion control shoes.

In addition to Lieberman's hypothesis, an 'evolutionary hypothesis' added further weight to the barefoot running ideology. The evolutionary hypothesis was that humans were made to run barefoot and had been doing so successfully for centuries before the advent of the modern running shoe.

Barefoot running advocates proposed that over time, humans evolved with adaptations that made barefoot running both suitable and less injurious.

Barefoot running advocates claimed that running barefoot was more efficient than running in motion control shoes. Given that we know that even 100 grams of additional shoe weight carries an added oxygen cost to the runner, this claim does have merit.

However, the ideology that every runner should move towards barefoot running is I believe unfounded and extreme. There remains a lack of conclusive evidence proving or refuting the proposed advantages of barefoot running.

A recent scientific review of barefoot running stated that:

> Little is known about barefoot running and injury and performance. The current promotion of barefoot running is based on oversimplified, poorly understood, equivocal and, in some cases, absent research, but remains a trend in popular media based on an evolutionary/epidemiological hypothesis and anecdotal evidence.[11]

If all runners abandoned their running shoes in favour of barefoot running, I believe it would be highly problematic. Many runners did transition away from their motion control shoes when the minimalist shoe trend emerged and, sadly, many of these same runners ended up with injuries. The three most common injuries I observed were Achilles tendon injuries, calf injuries, and stress reaction injuries to the metatarsal bones of the feet. My clinical observations were matched by research findings with several studies reporting that barefoot running was found to increase the risk of developing stress fractures of the long toe bones (metatarsals),[12] and injury to the Achilles tendon and calf muscles.[13]

I observed this injury spike between 2009 and 2012, when *Born to Run* was at its zenith in popularity. These injuries appeared to be the result of inappropriate transitioning from motion control shoes to barefoot running or lightweight minimalist running shoes.

Categorising a minimalist shoe

So what is a minimalist shoe, and what determines whether it is classified as minimalist? One of the difficulties in categorising minimalist running shoes is that there are no agreed upon standards of what constitutes a minimalist running shoe.

In general terms, any shoe that has an intentional reduction in the amount of shoe material between the runner's foot and the ground could be classified as a minimalist shoe. Minimalist shoes are produced with reduced midsole thickness and stiffness, reduced arch stability and support features, reduced stiffness in the heel, and a lower pitch (slope) of the shoe from heel to toes. Minimalist shoes are the opposite of motion control shoes in the majority of their features, but particularly in the amount of support and cushioning that they provide. Minimalist shoes offer only a little bit of grip and a thin layer of rubber to protect the sole of the foot.

RunBlogger and *Tread Lightly* author Peter Larson defined a minimalist shoe succinctly when he defined a barefoot shoe as *one that more closely approximates the barefoot condition.* Larson was also quoted as saying that he doesn't view minimalist as a 'category' of shoes per se – rather it was at the end of the cushioning of shoes spectrum. That is, at one end of the spectrum you have barefoot and at the other end you have maximally cushioned shoes, with minimalist shoes coming in closer to the barefoot end of this spectrum. I define a minimalist shoe as any shoe that has less than a 10-millimetre heel height.

McDougall mentions a running shoe named the Vibram FiveFingers in his bestseller *Born to Run*. These shoes are as minimalistic in design as a shoe can get. They have a rubber covering of the sole of the foot and a lightweight upper material that looks similar to a surfing bootie. They are the closest shoe that a runner can wear to approximate running barefoot, outside of running barefoot.

As book sales for *Born to Run* rocketed so did interest and subsequent sales in the Vibram FiveFingers. The response to *Born to Run*, and the sudden revolt away from traditional motion control running shoes towards a more barefoot approach, left the major shoe manufacturing giants losing market share. Realising that the boom and interest in barefoot running ideologies was not going away, the shoe manufacturing giants quickly bought to market their own versions of 'barefoot shoes' (an oxymoron, I know).

Nike came out with their Free range of shoes – with McDougall describing the first edition of the Nike Free as a 'swooshed slipper' and 'Nike's attempt to make a buck of a naked foot'. These acted as a forerunner for the scores of other minimalist shoes that would follow. It wasn't long before the other major shoe manufactures countered with their line of minimalist shoes too. The minimalist war was on, and models of lightweight shoes were churned out. Meanwhile shoe sales for more traditional motion control shoes plummeted.

Interestingly, according to *SportsOneSource* research in the first two years of this decade (2010–2012), sales of minimalist footwear were the fastest growing segment in the running shoe market. By 2011 in the US alone, sales of minimalist running shoes had nearly quintupled to $157 million.

What does the future hold for running shoe manufacturing?

Despite the rapid growth that the minimalist shoe market enjoyed from the mid-1990s onwards, it appears as though the minimalist shoe boom has ended. Minimalist shoes were the only segment in the $7 billion running shoe industry to post a decline in 2013. *SportsOneSource* research confirmed that minimalist shoe sales fell by a third to $220 million. Even so, the running shoe market is still trending towards simpler and more lightweight conventional shoes. I personally believe that this trend towards lighter shoes is a good legacy of the minimalist era.

I believe one reason for the downturn of minimalist shoe sales is that minimalist running shoes were pitched by the manufacturers as being a panacea for common running injuries that plagued modern-day runners. Unfortunately the outcomes experienced by many runners didn't match the expectations or claims set by the shoe manufacturers. The science has now caught up with the hype created by the manufacturers of minimalist shoes, and the science shows that the proposed advantages haven't been experienced by all runners. Many runners instead found themselves with a new set of complaints, including blisters and calf pain. As a result, many runners have returned to shoes that combine elements of motion control shoes with the lightweight designs characterised by pure minimalist shoes.

At the time of writing, the manufacturers of Vibram FiveFingers have just settled a class action filed against them. This class action contested that the company had deceived consumers by advertising that the FiveFingers could reduce foot injuries and strengthen foot muscles. However, because the manufacturers of Vibram FiveFingers' assertions were not based on scientific evidence, digruntled consumers received compensation for their shoe purchases.

A shoe selection framework

Now that we have examined the key periods in the evolution of running shoes, let's take a look at how to best select a running shoe based on research and my clinical experience.

In self-selecting a running shoe, it is important to note that you are not looking for the 'perfect running shoe'. Rather, several shoes or, in fact, a 'category' or shoe type will likely be suitable and your best solution.

As was mentioned earlier in this chapter, the prescription of shoes based on the three basic foot types was found in 2008 by researchers to not be supported by scientific evidence.[14] So, if selecting a pair of shoes based on a runner's basic foot type is not supported by scientific evidence, what is the running shoe consumer to base a decision on?

The answer is really quite simple. The following six key considerations need to be considered when making your next running shoe purchase.

Consideration 1: Comfort

Yes, that's right – comfort! When it comes to making an appropriate running shoe selection comfort is important. How often have you tried a pair of shoes on, walked a few steps in them, bounced up and down in the shoes, and thought to yourself, 'These are comfortable'? If you have had this experience, you are actually well on your way to making a good shoe purchase decision. According to UK sports podiatrist Ian Griffiths, comfort is linked to a reduction in injury frequency. So buying a running shoe based on comfort alone is the first key consideration. Simple.

Consideration 2: Shoe width

In selecting running shoes, shoe width is also important. It used to be that when you purchased a pair of shoes the shoe sales-person would bring out a metallic foot-width measuring device. (I'm sure you can recall going to a shoe store and having your foot width and length measured.) Today, though, for a reason I'm not aware of, the width of the foot is no longer measured.

Without this measurement, the running shoe consumer must rely on the 'feel' of the shoe width. Care must be taken as you do not want your foot to be too loose by selecting a shoe that is too wide in the forefoot (toe box) region. Likewise, you do not want to select a shoe that is too tight, either. Aim for a shoe width that is both 'snug' enough in the toe box, but still has sufficient room for the foot to swell and move.

Different shoe brands will differ with their shoe width. For example, the width of ASICS will differ from Nike, which will differ again from Brooks. In trying to find what brand is best for your foot, I suggest trying different shoes from different running shoe manufacturers to discover what feels most comfortable. Remember, comfort is the first consideration for selecting an appropriate running shoe. This will represent a better strategy for making a good shoe choice than being loyal to a particular brand. Keep in mind that some shoe brands, such as ASICS, allow you to order extra-wide shoes in a preferred shoe model.

Consideration 3: Stack height

Stack height is the third consideration when selecting running shoes. A shoe's stack height refers to the amount of cushioned shoe material (sole) that exists between the ground and the foot. Two different stack heights are often described: the forefoot stack height and the rear-foot stack height (see following figure).

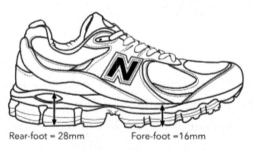

Rear-foot = 28mm   Fore-foot =16mm

Stack height

A shoe's stack height is different to its pitch or heel drop (see the following section). Conventional motion control shoes often have a rear-foot stack height of greater than 30 millimetres, while minimalist type shoes will often have a rear-foot stack height of approximately 10 millimetres. By having lower stack heights, the minimalist shoes provide for more foot awareness of the surface that the runner is running on.

So how do you choose a stack height that is best for you? The good news is that there is no hard and fast rule. The bad news is that there is no hard and fast rule!

Getting the stack height of your running shoes correct comes down to trial and error. I suggest you trial a pair of shoes, taking note of how they make you feel and, of course, any potential niggles that may develop. Keep trialling shoes until you find what you feel works best for you. If you still lack confidence in your selection, I suggest consulting a health professional and seeking their advice (e.g. a physio or podiatrist). However, care must be taken to not be too radical in experimenting. Avoid going from a shoe with a large stack height to a very small one too quickly, as this may result in problems such as unwanted injuries.

Consideration 4: Pitch or 'heel drop'

The fourth key consideration when making a shoe selection is the shoe's pitch or 'heel drop'. The terms 'shoe pitch' and 'heel drop' are interchangeable – 'heel drop' has simply become the popular term for what the footwear industry would typically call shoe 'pitch'. The terms describe the distance or height between the rear-foot stack height and the forefoot stack height. In other words, they describe the degree of the shoe's 'slope' or the shoe's gradient (see the following image).

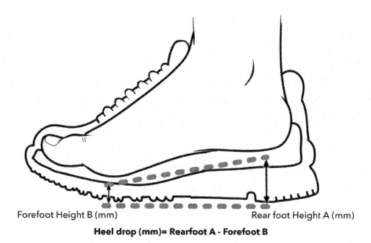

Forefoot Height B (mm)   Rear foot Height A (mm)

Heel drop (mm)= Rearfoot A - Forefoot B

Historically, the bulk of running shoes have had a heel drop of 10 millimetres. Craig Payne, on his blog Run Research Junkie, states that no research, theories, arguments, or rationale exists as to why 10 millimetres has been the standard. He writes that it just appears to be what most runners are comfortable with. All the major shoe manufacturers design shoes with a 10-millimetre drop. Craig writes that he was unable to find any blanket recommendations for the best heel drop for runners.[15]

With the advent and popularisation of minimalist shoes, the term 'zero drop' has become part of the running shoe vocabulary. However, no research exists to substantiate a zero-drop shoe being superior to a more traditional shoe with a 10-millimetre drop. The rationale for zero-drop shoes from manufacturers is that the zero-drop shoes facilitate a more 'natural' running technique – that is, away from a heel-strike. The assumption being that 10-millimetre drop running shoes facilitate a heel striking running form. However, anyone who has observed runners wearing either a zero-drop or a 10-millimetre drop running shoe will recognise that it is still possible to heel-strike in either a conventional shoe or a minimalist shoe. This renders the claims made by some minimalist shoe manufacturers that runners will shift to a whole or mid-foot strike when running in minimalist shoes as questionable.

So how do you select the correct heel drop or pitch for your next running shoe purchase? The ideal heel drop is runner-specific. There is no 'one size fits all'! There is no conclusive research that shows either a zero-drop or 10-millimetre drop shoe as being superior for either running performance or injury minimisation. As a result, and as with my recommendation for selecting the shoe's stack height, I suggest you experiment with different heel drop heights.

Some runners will do better in a zero-drop shoe, while others will do better in a 10-millimetre drop shoe. Once you discover what feels best, you can quite simply stick with what 'feels right' for you. As Craig Payne cites, there is no systematic ideal height but rather a subject-specific ideal height. To find your individual best heel drop, you must experiment with different shoe heel drops.

Consideration 5: Stiffness in the forefoot and mid-foot

The fifth key consideration when selecting a pair of running shoes is to consider the shoes' forefoot stiffness. It is my opinion that over time all runners should aim to move towards a lighter pair of running shoes. However, when selecting a lighter running shoe it is important to choose a shoe that has some degree of stiffness in the forefoot. Why? Well because stiffness in the forefoot appears to be consistent with better running performance.

Researchers propose that having a stiffer midsole of the shoe can increase the 'rebound' a runner's foot gets at the time of toe off (the final phase of foot push-off). The research asserts that this increase in rebound due to a stiffer midsole of a shoe can improve a runner's economy.[16]

The importance of having some mid-foot and forefoot shoe stiffness is evident when you look at the racing spikes worn by track runners. The shoes have rigid plastic that reinforces the forefoot with the aim of reducing the wasted energy for high-speed running at the point of the runner's toe off.

Therefore, when you go to a lighter shoe you should still feel the 'rebound' from the surface you are running on. The shoe should not be too soft, floppy, or thin in the forefoot. If it is, the runner will be wasting energy at the time of toe off, which will likely reduce running economy and therefore running speed.

Consideration 6: Moving towards lighter weight shoes

The final consideration when selecting your shoes is to consider the weight of the shoes. Elite runners know the benefits of running in lightweight shoes. This is why they race in lightweight racing flats – although they will often train in a heavier shoe than what they race in.

The key with transitioning to a lighter shoe is to not make the transition too quickly. In order to make a successful transition to a lighter shoe, runners must be prepared to be patient. (Unfortunately, patience is a virtue I often find many runners lack!) There will be a transition period required in getting used to the new running 'state' of wearing lighter shoes. This transition period will differ between all athletes in terms of method and time. There are no reliable set generalised formulas available that instruct how to integrate lighter-weight running shoes into a weekly running training program.

In order to make a sensible transition to lighter-weight running shoes, I suggest making progressive shoe purchases whereby each successive shoe gets lighter over time. For example, it may take a runner 18 to 24 months to arrive at the pair of shoes that best suits them in terms of weight. In this example a runner may transition through two to three pairs of shoes, before arriving at a shoe that is not too heavy, and not too light.

I suggest runners begin to transition to lighter and more minimalist shoes if they:

> know their body (that is, their mobility status and run screening results – refer to chapter 5)

> are regularly performing the home exercises that target the weaknesses identified as part of their running screening (refer to chapter 5) and, therefore, are making the running body more robust and able to deal with the loads of running in lighter shoes

> are not currently rehabilitating an injury

> are in a steady and unchanging part of a training regime (that is, as an example, not starting to run more volume or hills).

The preceding list includes my top tips for runners transitioning to lighter shoes; however, it excludes what I believe to be the keystone of making a successful transition to lighter shoes – that is performing daily calf raises.

Good calf endurance allows a runner to absorb the extra work the calves will do when running in a more minimalist or lighter shoe. I recommend all runners do 30 single-leg calf raises a day on each leg in order to facilitate better calf endurance, and to lower injury risk. When doing the calf raises, it is important to not do them too quickly. Care should be taken to push through the first and second toe of the foot and to take two to three seconds to do one single repetition. Most runners will struggle with this when they first attempt this exercise, but persistence pays off. (See www.pogophysio.com.au/book-resources.)

A common question I get asked is when to stop going lighter in weight with shoe selections. I suggest a runner stops transitioning to lighter shoes when they are running pain and injury free! Otherwise, if they consistently adhere to their body maintenance work and avoid training errors, they can go ahead and experiment with lighter shoes.

However, a runner should select heavier, more traditional and supportive, shoes if they:

> have an existing Achilles tendon or calf injury – if they go to a lighter shoe with a lesser heel height with these types of injuries, they will likely add additional load to these already painful and sensitive areas, which will, in most instances, aggravate the injury and exacerbate the pain experienced

> are comfortable in a heavier shoe and are enjoying pain- and injury-free running

> are able to consistently run with a cadence of 90 steps/ min and also exhibit the four other key principles of good running technique (correct foot placement, minimising excessive bopping, optimal body positioning, and utilisation of the natural leg springs – refer to chapter 5).

General shoe advice

Before we conclude step three of the five steps to pain- and injury-free running, let's also take a brief look at some general shoe advice – such as when is the best time to replace running shoes, common footwear errors, and how to prolong the life of your shoes.

Knowing when to replace your running shoes

In advising runners on when to replace running shoes, I tend to stay clear of nominating the commonly espoused method of a set amount of kilometres run in a shoe as the guide for when to replace running shoes. Given the variability between runners and their needs, I find it impractical to nominate a shoe's use-by date based on the volume of kilometres it has supported.

I suggest a better approach is to be guided by the following three principles for when to replace running shoes:

1 *The shoe can be folded in half.* If a running shoe can fold or bend in half, the shoe has passed its use-by date. I suggest retiring such shoes or assigning them to garden duties! Runners put themselves at unnecessary risk of developing injuries if they continue to run in old shoes.

2   *A runner is experiencing shin or general leg soreness.* The onset of shin or lower leg soreness is often the result of running in old and unsupportive running shoes. Typically this soreness will be experienced on the bottom one-third and the inside of the shin or the lower leg in general (i.e. in the calf muscles).

3   *The shoe starts to feel 'boggy'.* If running shoes lose the 'bounce factor' or springiness that they had when they were still providing appropriate levels of support, they are ready to be replaced. Many runners get a sense of this being the case, but continue to run in such shoes, which can quickly escalate the onset of injury.

Footwear errors to avoid

In addition to selecting running shoes based on sound principles and not popular fads or advice, it is also important to avoid making the following general running-shoe errors:

>   *Changing shoes just before a race.* Many runners panic about their shoe selection leading into a major or important running event. (Don't panic, stick with what you know.) Blisters are a common side effect from racing or training in a new pair of shoes. No runner wants the pain of blisters when racing or training.

>   *Believing that the most expensive running shoe is the best choice.* The most expensive shoes often do not constitute the 'best' shoe for every runner. Quite often the shoe with the highest price tag is the maximum stability shoe in that particular shoe range. Such shoes are typically bulky and

heavy motion control shoes. When a runner has gained knowledge of steps one and two of the five step run-pain-free process (chapters 5 and 6), running in a heavy motion control shoe may not actually be required. The runner may, in fact, be better served by selecting lighter shoes that are often a lesser price than the maximum motion control shoes.

> *Wearing shoes for too long.* Many runners run in their shoes for too long, and resist spending money to replace their old shoes. Running in old shoes increases the runner's lower limb injury risk. The effect of this is an overloading of the bony and soft tissue structures of the lower limbs. Typically the toes or shins will begin to become sore. Refer to the preceding section for more on when to replace your shoes.

> *Racing and training in the same shoes.* I encourage runners, where possible, to race in a lightweight shoe (for performance) and to train in something more supportive and of a heavier weight. Because the period of time spent in a racing shoe is only small relative to the overall time spent training, the wearing of lighter running shoes does not tend to create problems or injuries.

Tips to prolong the life of your shoes

Once you have selected your new pair of shoes, the following tips will help you get the best shelf life, maximise your investment, and maximise the performance of your shoes:

> *Always undo the laces when taking the shoes off.* Undoing the laces prolongs the integrity of the heel of the shoe, which, in turn, helps the entire shoe maintain its support and function.

> *Evenly tension your laces from bottom to top.* Evenly tensioning the laces of a running shoe ensures an even spread of torque (or force transmission) through the shoes. I suggest ensuring that the tension in the laces is evenly spread, which will avoid pressure points that can affect the foot's comfort in the shoe.

> *Use all of the shoelace eyelets.* Using all of the eyelets of the shoes will assist in foot stability. It will also prevent excessive and unwanted movement of the foot in the shoes. Many runners do not lace up the top holes of the shoe and this can create unwanted movement of the foot in the shoe.

> *Purchase a second pair of running shoes.* I suggest purchasing a second pair of running shoes (where the budget allows) and running in different shoes over alternate sessions. By alternating running shoes, a runner is able to note when one pair of shoes feels a bit 'tired', or has lost some support. This can alert the runner to replace their running shoes earlier than if they were running in only a single pair.

> *If travelling, include shoes in the carry-on luggage.* If travelling, I suggest runners don't squash their shoes inside their overflowing check-on bag. Squashing running shoes into a heavily packed suitcase or bag will deform the

shoes, which will have an adverse effect on their integrity and performance.

After checking out the following key points, you can move onto step four – the importance of hip stability.

Step 3: Navigate the footwear maze – key points

Here are the key points to remember from this chapter:

> Getting the correct or 'perfect' running shoe is often perceived by runners to be the panacea for avoiding all running injuries. This is not the case – running technique, and knowledge of one's running body should always precede shoe selection.

> Selecting an appropriate pair of running shoes needs to extend beyond matching a runner's foot type to a given pair of shoes. The 'wet foot' test has now fallen out of vogue. It is important to match the 'runner', and not just the runner's 'foot', to a shoe. Considerations such as injury history, running history, training schedule, and upcoming events need to be considered in the prescription of a running shoe.

> A runner will often be well suited to a 'category' of running shoes as opposed to just one particular style of running shoes. This means you are not shopping for a single shoe, but rather you are looking for a

---

Step 3: Navigate the footwear maze – key points (continued)

cluster of shoes that may share similar characteristics (for example, they are light, have a heel drop of 10 millimetres, and have a moderate stack height).

> Pronation is a normal and healthy foot movement required to absorb impact forces when a runner lands. The link between pronation and injury development and treatment is scientifically not well understood. A foot that pronates excessively may or may not need to be controlled through running shoes that have anti-pronation features. I suggest seeking the advice of a physiotherapist or podiatrist in order for the best assessment and recommendation to be made.

> Not all excessively pronating feet require orthotics. The decision as to whether orthotics are required is best made by a health professional such as a physiotherapist or podiatrist, after they have taken into account many considerations about the runner's body, their biomechanics, and their running goals and running history.

> When purchasing your next pair of shoes, focus on the six key shoe selection considerations: comfort, shoe width, stack height, heel drop, forefoot stiffness, and moving towards lighter shoes slowly over time, in order to self-select an appropriate running shoe.

Case study: Janette

Janette presented with an ongoing Achilles tendon problem brought about by a sudden increase in running volume. Janette was a middle-age and very fit woman, who just two years prior had been introduced to the sport of triathlon by her friend.

Based on my initial assessment, Janette needed to work on her running body by starting with strengthening her calf muscles and also her hip-stability muscles. Janette's running technique was also analysed and it was found that Janette was overstriding somewhat, not leaning forwards with her trunk, and also lacking hip stability.

The clinical diagnosis was mid-portion Achilles tendinopathy. Ultrasound imaging confirmed this diagnosis and other possible diagnoses, such as bursitis and inflammation of the tendon sheath (paratenonitis), were excluded.

Hip and calf strengthening exercises, and tendon rehabilitative exercises were prescribed. Run technique coaching was also completed. Janette was also instructed to reduce her overall volume of running and to avoid speed work until the symptoms settled.

In addition, I recommended that Janette stick with her conventional running shoes until the symptoms eased and the tendon structure and function improved. Once this was achieved, Janette slowly transitioned into a slightly lighter running shoe, within the same brand of shoes that she was used to.

The lighter shoe afforded Janette better technique and what was more (self-reported) awareness of running technique, and foot positioning on impact. Transitioning to the lighter shoes was

Case study: Janette (continued)

achievable because it was done over the course of six months, and with regular completion of single-leg calf raises. This allowed the tendon and calf to deal with the greater workload that running in a lighter shoe produced.

Janette has since gone on to complete many triathlons, including half ironman events, and has even represented Australia at the World Age Group Triathlon Championships. Janette has no ongoing Achilles tendon problems or symptoms.

Appropriate running shoe prescription, and later self-selection, was a key component in Janette's success.

Chapter 8

STEP 4: The importance of hip stability

Step 1: Discover your running body

Step 2: Run with great technique

Step 3: Navigate the footwear maze

Step 4: The importance of hip stability

Step 5: The power of rest

It's all in the hips!

So far you have covered three of the five steps to running pain and injury free, and also faster. You have discovered your running body, learnt how to run with great technique, and discovered how to navigate the footwear maze.

You are now ready for the fourth step to running pain and injury free – ensuring that you run with a controlled and stable pelvis.

Running with a controlled and stable pelvis will be courtesy of the development of hip muscles that are both strong and have good endurance. As a runner, you need to be able to run without your pelvis (or hips) moving around excessively. In physio parlance, I refer to such minimising of hip or pelvic movement as a runner having sufficient 'hip stability'.

When you achieve running with a stable pelvis (hips), your injury risk will be minimised and faster running will also result.

Running is a single-leg sport

Before we look at the role that hip stability plays in fast and injury-free running, let's consider something about running that often goes unrecognised: that is that running is actually a technically demanding sport. It may not appear to be that way. After all, don't we just put on our shoes and go for a run?

Well, as you discovered in step 2 (Run with great technique), running is a lot more involved than that. You now know that certain principles and characteristics typify great running technique, such as a runner's: body position, minimal bopping up and down movements, foot placement, and running cadence.

If we back away from the characteristics of great running technique and focus on the fundamental movement components required to run, we discover an interesting and often overlooked finding: that running is actually a single-leg sport! Let me explain.

When you run, you are in effect 'bouncing' from one leg to the next. If you study the running motion, you will see that the feet of a runner are never concurrently on the ground. You land on your right leg, absorb the load of the landing, produce force through muscle contraction and activation with the right leg muscles, and finally push off on the right leg. You then land on the left leg, and repeat the process.

If you were to do the maths in order to calculate the number of times you land on each leg, assuming that you are now running at the ideal cadence of 90 steps/min, it would look like this:

Running for one hour (60 minutes):
60×90 steps/min = 5,400 steps/min

That means that, during a typical one-hour run, you will land on each leg a staggering 5,400 times! Extrapolated to two hours of running, that is 10,800 foot strikes or landings for each leg. Over, say, a four-hour marathon, that number would be up to 21,600 foot strikes and landings. To put this in perspective, if a runner runs 30 kilometres in training every week, this volume will equate to approximately 1 to 1.5 million foot strikes per year! (Assuming the runner was running at 5–6 min/km pace, and ran for 52 weeks of the year.)

Being mindful that running is a single-leg sport with multiple leg landings allows us to appreciate the degree to which a runner's hips need to be both stable and strong. Without hip stability, a runner going out for an hour run, making 5,400 landings on each leg, may soon be headed for trouble in the form of injury development.

What is 'hip stability'?

'Hip stability' refers to the ability of the muscles around the hips and pelvis to minimise excessive and unwanted movements of the hips and pelvis when performing a task or certain movement. In this case, the movement is the running motion.

For our purposes we are interested in the role that the hip muscles play in generating hip stability during the running motion. While the hip muscles play a role in stabilising the hips during the airborne phase of running (that is, when the body is in full flight in between leg landings), the hip muscles' chief role is to stabilise the runner's hip when the runner lands alternately on each leg.

One concept of hip stability is to think of it as being a subset of 'core stability'. Most people are familiar with the notion of having a strong core. They recognise the importance of having good core stability. In clinical practice, clients regularly self-identify that one of their contributing factors in the onset of their running injuries, postural problems, or lower back pain is likely their 'weak core'. Although they often do not fully understand the finer detail of how weakness of their core has in part contributed to their injury, just the fact that they know that core stability is important illustrates that most people are familiar with the concept and importance of having adequate core stability and a good 'core'.

The term 'core stability' pertains to having adequate muscular support of the lower back and pelvic girdle. Muscles required for core stability include the well-recognised abdominal muscles (rectus abdominis or 'six pack' muscles), oblique muscles (diagonal muscles on our sides), transversus abdominis (deep stomach muscle), and lower back extensor muscles (erector spinae and multifidus). The figures opposite show these muscles.

Core stability of the trunk and lower back is required for the efficient and safe performance of all activities of daily living including running. In musculoskeletal medicine and physiotherapy, we often refer to core stability as being 'lumbo-pelvic' stability – that is, the regions of the hips and lower (lumbar) spine are 'corseted' and protected from unwanted and excessive movements by the surrounding musculature.

In running terms, having the hips and lower back stabilised by the core stability muscles will result in improved running economy, because the runner is expending less energy (by avoiding unnecessary movements) with each landing. As you are now aware, the effect of improved running economy is faster running, which is a great outcome and benefit of a runner having stable hips.

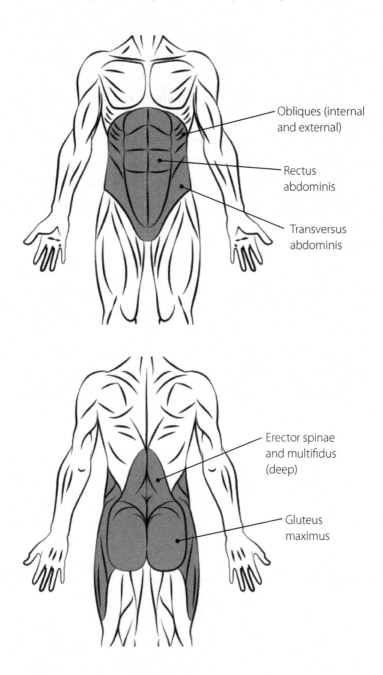

Obliques (internal
and external)

Rectus
abdominis

Transversus
abdominis

Erector spinae
and multifidus
(deep)

Gluteus
maximus

Such hip stability produced through having appropriate activity and strength in the hip and core muscles also results in a much reduced lower limb injury risk. We will shortly explore the connection between hip stability and injury risk in more detail.

For runners who actively seek to improve their core stability, great emphasis is often placed on the development of abdominal and trunk muscle strength and activation. Exercises such as side bridges, front planks, abdominal crunches, and sit ups are commonplace in gyms and as part of recreational athletes' home exercise programs.

While such a focus on the development of trunk muscle activation and strength is important, the activation, strength and endurance of the hip muscles must not be ignored! I have observed that the majority of runners are not aware of the difference between hip stability and core stability, and so they fail to recognise the need to develop hip stability.

The muscles that serve to stabilise the hips are shown in the following figure.

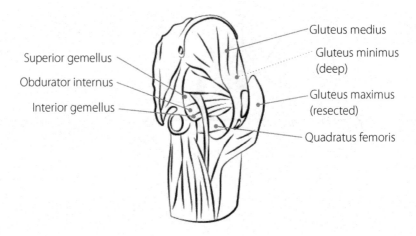

Superior gemellus

Obdurator internus

Interior gemellus

Gluteus medius

Gluteus minimus (deep)

Gluteus maximus (resected)

Quadratus femoris

Essentially, these hip stability muscles serve to perform one of three actions summarised in the following table.

Hip movement	Muscles involved	Importance to a runner	If deficient in strength
Extend the hip	Gluteus maximus	High	Runner will look like they are sitting in a chair; that is, they will not appear to be running tall. This will result in a shortened stride length, and over activity of the lower back muscles.
Externally rotate the hip	Gemelli (superior and interior), obturator internus, quadratus femoris, gluteus maximus	High	Runner's hips will drop down and inwards (internal rotation of the hip); that is, the hip will appear to 'collapse' on the leg that is impacting the ground.
Laterally support the hip	Gluteus medius and minimus	High	Runner's hips will sway sideways excessively – think of a model on a catwalk whose hips move from side to side, on the leg that is impacting the ground.

All three of the hip stability movements included in the preceding table need to be controlled by hip muscles that are strong enough to support a runner's training load. These muscles must also have enough endurance to be able to stabilise the pelvis for upwards of thousands of repetitions over the course of a runner's week of training. If the muscles supporting one or more of the three key hip movements (hip extension, external rotation, and sideways or lateral support) are deficient, a runner will not have adequate hip stability and will, therefore, not run to their true potential.

In practice I find that many runners commonly have sufficient activity in one or even two groups of muscles, but are deficient in the third group of muscles. I routinely discover weaknesses and poor activation, primarily in the muscles responsible for hip external rotation. When hip external rotation activation and strength is either minimal or below par, the runner's hips will collapse inwards on each single-leg landing, exposing the athlete to adverse loads through the legs, and slowing the runner down. Because hip external rotation muscle activity and strength is so important hip external rotation is included as one of the eight measures completed during your running screening (see chapter 5).

Why is hip stability so important?

Hip stability is critical for fast running as well as injury prevention and rehabilitation. Let's take a closer look.

Hip stability and faster running

When you consider that for every hour of running, you will make contact with the ground 5,400 times, it is clear why having sound and strong hip stability is of paramount importance to the runner looking to run pain and injury free.

The hip muscles of a runner need to be able to withstand the loading that comes with the repetitive impact of a runner's legs and body in the form of repetitive ground reaction forces. Impact in the vicinity of up to two to three times a runner's body weight must be absorbed.

If the hip muscles are not sufficiently strong, the runner's pelvis will 'collapse' on single-leg landing at the time of impact. The effect of this collapsing and excessive and unwanted movement of the runner's pelvis is a slowing down of the runner with each and every leg landing. A collapsing pelvis requires more time to collapse and go through its range of motion than a pelvis that is strong and absorbs the loading on impact. A pelvis that is well supported by strong hip muscles will not collapse, and therefore helps one leg spring quickly and efficiently off the ground before landing on the opposite leg.

Although this slowing down brought about by a collapsing pelvis will be in milliseconds and may appear to be inconsequential, if you add up even an additional one hundredth of a second per leg landing (due to insufficient hip muscle strength) across an hour run, that is an additional 36 seconds for each leg across an hour of running! Saving this time can be achieved by not training any harder or running further, but by simply having hip muscles that are 'strong enough' to provide adequate stability to the runner's pelvis and hips.

In 2009, researchers discovered that six weeks of core strength training improved 5,000-metre running times for the runners who received the core strength training compared with those who did not.[1] Several of the prescribed exercises included in the training program given to the runners receiving core strength training targeted hip stability and strength. The runners who participated in this study were preparing for a marathon, and they underwent four sessions of five core exercises for the six weeks.

Hip stability, injury minimisation and injury rehabilitation

Excessive hip motion during running represents a major injury risk factor for runners. When a runner's hips move excessively due to hip muscle weakness, the legs of the runner will be subjected to greater loading and strain.

Numerous research findings verify the link between hip muscle strength (and pelvic stability) and the onset of running injuries. For example, hip adduction (where the hip moves towards the midline of the body) and internal rotation (a collapsing in of the hip towards the runner's midline – see following figure) have been associated with knee pain and iliotibial band syndrome.[2,3,4] Altered hip movements and reduced hip strength have also been identified as common findings in females with knee pain.[5]

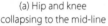

(a) Hip and knee
collapsing to the mid-line

(b) Hip and knee neutral –
little collapsing to the mid-line

Research has also shown that females have a greater tendency to core instability than males, which may predispose females to greater incidence of lower extremity injury.[6] One group of researchers found that female athletes displayed significantly decreased hip external rotation and side bridge strength measures compared with their male counterparts.[7] They reported that athletes who experienced an injury over the course of a season displayed significant weakness in hip abduction and external rotation. They also concluded that hip external rotation was the sole significant predictor of injury status for the athletes they tested. They tested 80 female and 60 male athletes, many of whom were cross country runners.

Given the frequency of running injuries (as discussed in chapter 4) a failure to stabilise a runner's pelvis may expose them to a gamut of running injuries. The good news is that stabilising the hips can be a straightforward process for a runner. With the right exercises, discipline and scoring method to gauge progress, I have found that all runners, irrespective of running ability, can stabilise their hips. I often tell runners who are either rehabilitating from injury, or seeking to prevent injury, that hip stability exercises are 'medicine' for a runner's legs. During this chapter, I will introduce you to some of the best exercises I prescribe to improve the hip stability of runners.

The 'hip down and foot up' approach

In my clinical experience the vast majority of running injuries typically involve a weakness of the hip muscles. The effect of this is an inability of the hip muscles to support the runner as they bound from one leg to the other. This muscular weakness of the hip muscles creates excessive loading of the runner's entire lower limb.

In practice, when I conduct my injury assessments I approach all lower limb running injuries with what I term my 'hip down and foot up' approach. This approach encapsulates the concept of multifactorial injury causation that I covered in chapter 4 (understanding the causes and effects of injury).

If, in assessing an injured runner, a therapist fails to look at the runner holistically, and instead takes a localised approach to the injured area, achieving a complete rehabilitation is not likely. This is because if all injury causative injury factors are not detected during the assessment of the injury, the runner will not address all of the required factors in their rehabilitation. So, when looking at lower limb injuries, one of my mantras is for therapists to always be looking for the 'hip down and foot up' possible causes of the running injury.

For example, in assessing a runner with knee pain, I need to assess both the foot and the hip function in order to be thorough and not miss a key contributory injury factor. Failure to assess both the foot's and the hip's possible contributions to the runner's knee pain could result in the oversight of key contributing factors that led to the development of the injury. Such an omission on assessment would then compromise the runner's rehabilitation and their likelihood of returning to pain- and injury-free running.

To further explain, the foot can negatively affect the knee if the foot over-pronates (see chapter 7). When the foot over-pronates, the result can be increased contact pressures behind the knee-cap (patella), and also increased pressures to the cartilage layer of the femur that lays underneath the knee-cap. These increased pressures can result in softening and sometimes injuries to the cartilage that lines the back side of the patella and the groove of the femur. When cartilage of one or both of these structures is irritated or damaged, the runner will likely experience knee pain. This is an example of the foot having a 'foot up' effect on the development of knee pain.

Similarly, weakness at the hip can negatively affect the knee joint by 'collapsing' (inwardly rotating and adducting) under the weight of the runner's body when the runner lands. This is what I refer to as the 'hip down' effect on the knee. The result of the hip collapsing is that the knee joint is exposed to excessive and adverse joint loading, which is the same effect that over-pronation of the foot has on knee joint loading. The result can be pain and injury development at the knee joint, because it is the region that is 'absorbing' the additional load from the dysfunctional movement of the runner's hip.

It is also possible in this example that the knee becomes sore from only a hip down (hip muscle weakness) deficit, with no foot involvement. The alternate scenario may also be possible – where the hip has no contribution and only the foot has a contribution. However, the injured athlete and the treating practitioner need to consider both the feet and the hips as potential injury contributory factors.

This hip down and foot up assessment approach also holds true when assessing running injuries other than knee pain. It is a fundamental approach required when assessing injuries such as the most common injuries we looked at in chapter 4 – that is, shin splints, hamstring injuries, runner's knee, Achilles tendon problems, and plantar fasciitis.

Failure to assess a running-related injury using this 'hip down and foot up' approach may result in key contributing injury factors being missed and therefore not rehabilitated.

The role of fatigue

In addition to sufficient activation and strength of the major hip stabilising muscles, a runner must also have adequate endurance of the hip musculature. In the absence of well-developed hip muscle endurance, when a runner fatigues – such as towards the end of a training run or towards the end of a running event – the loading through each leg will markedly increase.

As a runner fatigues, so do their hip muscles. When fatigue kicks in, the hip muscles lose their ability to counteract the forces associated with landing and, as a result, the hips start to 'drop' and collapse.

If you were to observe the end of a running event (provided the runners had given their 'all' and were fatigued as they entered the homestretch), you would notice that runners of all levels had a degree of hip collapsing occurring as they ran the home-straight towards the finish line. If you were to slow down the running motion of even the podium or place-getting runners with video analysis, you would discover some degree of hip collapsing occurring with even these runners.

If you were to then look at the back markers, or the last finishers in a running event, you would see a far greater degree of hip collapsing as these runners approached the finish line. In fact, if you were to watch from start to finish for all runners to cross the finish line (first place to last place), you would very likely observe that as running speeds decreased, hip stability levels also decreased – meaning that the further toward the back of the field a runner finished, the greater the degree of hip weakness that would be observable.

This indicates that hip stability plays a large and very important role in faster running, and not just in injury prevention and rehabilitation. The best defence against developing fatigue of the hip muscles is to work on the endurance and strength of the hip stability and core muscles that support running. This will be the focus of the rest of the chapter.

Analysing a runner with and without hip stability

When a runner has sufficient hip stability, their hip muscles will 'control' the movement of the hip and entire pelvis. The key hip muscles collectively have enough strength to prevent the 'collapsing' of the runner's hip when they land.

With sufficient hip stability, no downward or outward dropping away at the hip level of the leg that has just made impact with the ground occurs. This gives the appearance of hips or a pelvis that is 'level'. If a line were to be drawn across the top of the hips the line would be horizontal – see image (a) in the following figure.

In contrast, the runner who does not have sufficient hip stability will have hip muscles that are not strong or resilient enough to deal with the repetitive single-leg loading of running. Unlike the pelvis of the runner with sufficient hip stability (a), which stays horizontal, the pelvis of the runner with deficient hip stability will collapse outwards on landing. This will create an oblique or downward sloping line if it were to be drawn across the top of the pelvis to the opposite hip – which is responsible for the swing phase of the opposite leg. See image (b) in the following figure.

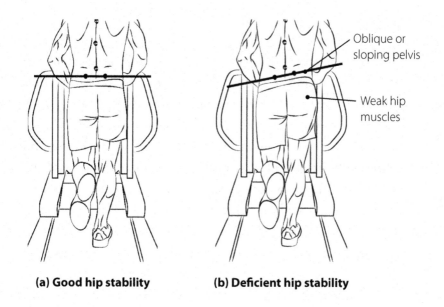

Oblique or
sloping pelvis

Weak hip
muscles

(a) Good hip stability   **(b) Deficient hip stability**

How to determine if you have adequate hip stability

You can determine whether or not you have sufficient hip stability to support your running in several ways. These can be broken into subjective and objective assessment methods. The following sections take a closer look at the ways to measure your hip stability.

Subjective tests

A number of subjective tests are available, as outlined in the following section.

(a) Video analysis

With the advent and widespread use and accessibility of technology, having a running video analysis performed has never been easier. Video analysis refers to capturing some footage of you running, in order to assess running technique. Outside of a professional video analysis of your running technique, I recommend capturing footage on a treadmill. This will result in more meaningful footage than if you were running down a road or path where you would quickly be out of sight to the video recorder. Note that while some differences in running technique exist between running on the treadmill and running on the road or footpath, these differences are relatively minor. They certainly will not detract from the purpose of a video analysis, which is to simply capture some footage of you running in order for you to assess your hip stability. You can choose to either do a video analysis with a friend or have one done by a health professional such as a physiotherapist.

If you are going to capture your running footage with a friend, I suggest that your friend uses a smart phone, which gives you the options of using a basic video mode or downloading a video analysis app. Many movement analysis apps are available free of charge, and the benefit of these apps is they will allow you to slow the video down and watch the footage as slow as one-eighth normal speed. Apps such as Ubersense and Coach My Video (readily available from Apple's App Store) provide the option of slow motion analysis (120 frames per second) and pausing of the footage. These apps allow you to draw lines over the body in order to analyse body angles. When the footage is slowed down you will be able to more accurately gauge the degree of movement in your hip at the time of single-leg landing.

I recommend you take two to three minutes of footage from behind and also two to three minutes from each side in order to get your side-on view. It's best to have the hips exposed – males running shirtless and females wearing a sports top or similar – to allow for the best and unencumbered analysis of the hip movements.

When being filmed, it is important to try to run normally or 'naturally'. Don't try to correct anything or change anything in an attempt to 'run better'. If you do this, you will defeat the purpose of the analysis. It's normal for runners to feel uneasy about the prospect of having running technique analysed by video. However, the benefits that come from the video analysis far outweigh the momentary unease of being in front of the video recorder!

When reviewing the footage taken from behind, look for evidence of hip 'drop' and collapsing of the pelvis. Slow the footage down, and pause the footage when a foot makes contact with the treadmill (stance leg). Now look up the leg (from the foot up towards the hip) to see if any of the following signs of poor hip stability are evident:

> stance hip is hitched up (that is, towards the lower back)

> stance hip is deviating out to the side, away from the body's midline

> knee is collapsing inwards towards the body's midline.

Alternately refer to the previous illustration (b) (analysing a runner with and without hip stability) as a guide for what to look for. Scroll through the footage and analyse each foot landing to see what each leg is doing. It is very common for even the world's best runners to have subtle side to side movements, or even at times quite marked discrepancies of hip and body movements. What is your left hip doing compared to your right hip? Does one side collapse more than the other side?

It is important to remember that in assessing just two to three minutes of running footage you will not be able to observe the known role that fatigue plays in movements of the hips.

Now that you have viewed the footage taken from behind, you can analyse the side-on footage. With this footage, you are looking for the following:

> *Where your foot makes impact with the ground relative to your body's centre of mass.* This is the same as assessing for overstriding when addressing running technique (refer to chapter 6). A runner who is overstriding will have their foot land out in front of their knee and the body's centre of mass. It is quite likely that the trunk will be tilted backwards when a runner is overstriding.

> *How high the heel of the swing leg (the leg that is in the air) travels upwards towards the bottom.* Runners who have good hip stability will have their heel come close towards the bottom of the swing leg (leg that is swinging). Meanwhile runners who collapse through their stance leg – due to weak or deficient hip stability – will have a more 'open' angle of their swing leg as it travels forwards, before it begins to extend in preparation for landing.

> *Excessive up and down movement ('bopping').* Look for how the runner's body moves in terms of how much

or how little the head moves up and down. Does the body appear to travel up and down excessively? Or, in contrast, is the body only moving up and down a little? While making an assessment of this in the absence of a benchmarked height is highly subjective, you will generally be able to tell if the runner is bopping up and down too much. It's important to note that when footage is being viewed in slow motion vertical movement of a runner's body appears more pronounced compared with when the runner is running in real time.

TIP: A quick note on video analysis: no-one likes what they see the first time their running technique is captured. It's similar to listening to your recorded voice being played back. I encourage you to embrace what you see; don't shy away from it. Like so many things in life, ignorance is rarely bliss. It is amazing how viewing your running technique courtesy of video footage helps you make positive changes to your running technique and therefore your performance. These changes are not possible, or are less likely to occur, if you're just relying on how you 'think' or 'feel' that you run.

(b) Partner feedback

Another way of subjectively assessing hip stability is to educate your running partner, or a member of your running group, about what to look for in assessing your hip stability. The things your running partner is looking for are the same assessment points analysed with video analysis, namely: collapsing of the stance leg on landing with the hip hitching up and out to the side, and the other hip dropping down. The challenge is that your running partner will not have the ability to replay footage, or watch the footage back in slow motion. As you run, have your partner run behind you at different stages of the run – the start, the middle portion, and the end. Ask your partner for feedback on what your hips are doing throughout the run. Despite the challenges of analysing technique while literally being on the run, one benefit of giving and getting such partner feedback is that the feedback is real-time. Feedback given by your running partner as you run will prove more useful than feedback given at the end of the run.

I suggest that doing video analysis and getting real-time partner feedback is a good combination. Don't forget to return the favour for your running partner!

(c) Take notice of how your body 'feels' when you run

If you routinely run alone and seldom run with a training partner, taking note of how your body 'feels' when you run will also give you some insight into your hip stability.

Consider the following: do you feel like your hips are collapsing each time your foot hits the ground? Or do you feel like you are quickly springing off the ground with each foot strike – with minimal hip drop occurring? Do you feel like you are running 'up tall', or do you feel like you are almost 'sitting down' as you run? These are helpful self-assessment points for any runner. Additionally, thinking about the five principles of great running technique (refer to chapter 6) will also be of use with this form of self-assessment.

(d) Use mirrors and glass

Another helpful self-assessment of your hip stability can be making it a habit to use any reflective glass or mirrors that you run past on your training runs for real-time visual feedback. Rows of shop fronts or even bus stops will often afford you the opportunity to observe (momentarily) your running technique and form. It may sound vain but regularly observing yourself in such a way will at least give you some degree of technique feedback. Don't be coy – go ahead and take a look. This real-time feedback can be very useful – as quick as it is!

(e) Review photos

Looking at and studying photos taken of you while you were either competing in an event or out training can be very useful. The bulk of photos will capture you with one leg impacting the ground. Most event photos will capture you from front on (such as a finishing shot or out on the course). Refer to the treadmill figures earlier in this chapter and determine the angle of your hips. Are they level? Or are they on an oblique (sloping) angle? The sloping of the hips indicates a deficiency of hip stability.

(f) Single-leg squat test

This test is performed by standing on a single leg. The leg that is not performing the squat is bent at the knee and not touching the ground. The steps of the test are as follows:

> Squat on the single leg without the support of anything to balance with or lean on.

> Squat as deeply as possible (your bottom doesn't need to go below your hips – this is too deep).

> Ask your observer or assessor to stand in front or behind you as you perform the squat. The observer is looking for:

>> upward hitching of the hip that is squatting

>> sideways (lateral) collapsing of the squatting hip (away from the midline of the body – i.e. outwards)

>> an inward collapsing of the knee of the squat leg towards the midline of the body

>> a lower hip height on the opposite leg that is lifted off the ground (producing a downward sloping pelvis).

> Repeat the test on the other leg.

See the following figure for an indication of how to perform a single-leg squat test. Refer also to a video of this test online at www.pogophysio.com.au/book-resources.

If your observer notices the signs included in the preceding list, this will indicate a deficiency of hip stability. The degree of hip instability can vary from mild to severe. This will be primarily due to weakness of the gluteus medius muscle. Ask your assessor to objectively classify you as having either: poor, adequate, or good hip stability – based on their observations.

To get a good idea of the relationship between fatigue and stability, you can repeat the squat twelve times and note if the hip drop gets more pronounced. Note that to get a true idea of hip stability over an hour run, the equivalent test would be to perform a series of 5,400 squats on each leg. I do not recommend this!

Objective tests

When it comes to any form of performance improvement, the adage that what can be measured can be improved is powerful. While the subjective measures of hip stability listed in the preceding section are both useful and important, getting an objective measurement of a runner's hip stability is critical.

In clinical practice, I witness runners make large improvements with their hip stability by undergoing initial objective testing of their hip stability, followed by subsequent retesting. The power of keeping score is evident in those who undergo objective testing compared with those who do not. These observations apply to both recreational and elite-level runners. I have found that runners of all levels are motivated to improve their hip stability by improving their 'scores'.

Objective testing should measure all three of the essential hip stability movements (extension, external rotation, and sideways or lateral support). While the preceding subjective assessments can be completed without the input of a health professional, the three tests outlined in the following section are best performed by a health professional such as physiotherapist. I suggest taking this book to a physiotherapist who has an interest in running and have them objectively assess your hip stability.

(a) Hip external rotation test

This test is the same as what was performed in your running screening (chapter 5). The test is performed with the runner sitting on the edge of a treatment table with the knee of the testing leg positioned at 90 degrees. Ideally a neatly folded towel is placed underneath the knee to keep the hip to knee angle at 90 degrees.

The steps of the test are as follows:

> The tester asks the runner to lift their foot inwards as far as they can towards the midline of their body.

> It is important that the tester looks for compensatory movements, such as lifting of the test hip up and off the table. Another compensatory movement pattern that will result in an incorrect measure is leaning the trunk in the opposite direction to which the foot is moving.

> The tester uses a measuring tool known as a goniometer (or joint angle measuring device) to measure the angle

that the shin or lower limb makes relative to an imaginary vertical line (the non-moving arm of the goniometer) that passes through the axis of the knee.

> Repeat the test three times to ensure an accurate measure has been made before testing the opposite side. Ideally, the scores or measures of each side would be symmetrical for each leg. Often though, a discrepancy exists in the measurements from each side. Such discrepancy of side to side scores can be a common finding for all levels of runners – beginners to the elite.

It is important and sobering to realise that a single measure of this test is the equivalent to the support needed for just one single-leg landing when running – let alone the 5,399 single leg landings that will follow with a one-hour training (assuming that the runner was running with a cadence of 90 steps per minute).

Interpretation

When interpreting the scores of each hip, the ideal angle to achieve is 40 degrees. A score of less than 40 degrees indicates that the hip stability muscles (the external rotators and gluteus maximus) do not have sufficient activation and strength. When weakness or inactivity of the hip external rotators is detected with this test, the runner will be experiencing hip collapsing as they run due to a deficiency of hip stability.

The following figure shows this test being performed. Refer also to the Hip External Rotation Test online as part of the

Running Screening video at www.pogophysio.com.au/book-resources.

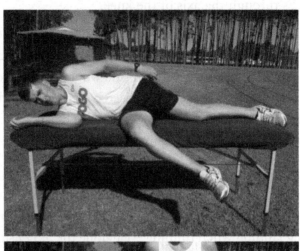

(b) Single-leg bridge hold test

This test is performed with the runner lying on the floor with one leg fully extended and the other leg bent with the foot flat on the ground. The bent leg should have the foot positioned just slightly in front of the knee, and the thigh of the extended leg should be parallel to the thigh of the bent leg (see following figure).

This test assesses strength and activation of the gluteus maximus (glut max). Glut max is the main muscle involved in hip extension and, when working well, glut max allows the runner to run tall and avoid looking like they are seated in a chair.

The steps of the test are as follows:

> The runner is asked to lift (or bridge) the hips upwards and maximally, until a virtual straight line is formed that bisects the knee, the hips, and the shoulder of the bridging leg.

> No sagging or 'drooping' of the pelvis is allowed.

> The runner is asked to hold this position for as long as possible while the tester times the bridge position.

> The tester stops the test when they notice that the runner's hips have started to sag towards the floor, or that the trunk/hips have started to twist, rotate, or collapse towards the leg that is bridging.

> Just as with the external rotation test, the tester will need to get a score for each side. Once again, the scores for each leg should ideally be symmetrical with no major side-to-side discrepancy.

Interpretation

When interpreting the test, keep in mind the goal is to be able to hold each side for 90 seconds without rotating the hips or dropping the bottom. Refer to www.pogophysio.com.au/book-resources for a video showing this test being performed.

(c) Side bridge hold test

This test is performed with the runner positioned on the floor or ground, on their side. The top foot is positioned over the top of the bottom leg and the elbow is directly underneath the shoulder, with the forearm resting at 90 degrees on the floor. The top hand can support the shoulder while bridging. The following figure shows this test being performed.

This test primarily assesses gluteus medius (glut med) strength. Additionally this test assesses the strength and endurance of the obliques, and other muscles that line the side of the body.

The gluteus medius is the main muscle involved in stabilising the lateral or sideways collapsing movement that occurs with a single-leg landing when hip stability is deficient. When the gluteus medius is strong and has good endurance, collapsing of the pelvis during landing is counteracted.

The steps of the test are as follows:

> The runner is asked to lift (or bridge) the hips upwards until a virtual straight line is formed from the ankle, through the hips, and into the shoulder.

> No sagging of the pelvis towards the floor is allowed.

> The runner is asked to hold this position for as long as possible while the tester times the bridge position.

> The tester stops the test when they notice that the hips have started to 'sag' or drop towards the floor, when the runner is finally unable to correct this noticeable sagging of the hips.

> The tester will need to get a score for each side. Once again, the scores should ideally be symmetrical with no major side-to-side discrepancy.

Interpretation

When interpreting this test, keep in mind that the goal time is holding the bridge position with good form, on each side, for 120 seconds. A score of 60 to 100 seconds is 'good'. A score of less than 60 seconds is 'poor'. Hold times should increase proportionately to the distance a runner plans to train or race – the further the distance, the longer the required hold time with this test. (See www.pogophysio.com.au/book-resources to access video of this test being performed.)

Improving your hip stability

If the preceding subjective and/or objective measures reveal that you have a deficiency of hip stability and strength, I have some good news for you! Improvements in hip stability can occur quite quickly for the runner who is dedicated to improving. Regular and consistent completion of several key hip stability exercises can yield timely results and improvements.

Improving hip stability involves three stages. The hip muscles need to first be activated, then strengthened, with the development of hip muscle endurance following thereafter.

The following flowchart demonstrates this.

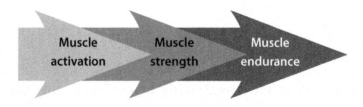

Delivering hip muscle activation

Muscle activation is the first stage of improving hip stability. I explain to runners that muscle activation is analogous to charging a car battery that has gone flat. In the same manner as the battery, the muscles required for hip stability can also go 'flat'. In medical terms, we call this an under-recruited muscle – that is, a muscle that does not get appropriately recruited for use. When corrective hip stability exercises are first being performed by a runner, they are normally activating or 'waking' up the muscle, or muscles, that have been dormant and improperly used for running.

An example of activation of a key running muscle is the activation of the gluteus maximus (bottom muscle). Many runners have glut max muscles that are under activated, and one of the chief reasons for this is that most runners (like most people) spend much of their time sitting on the glut max and, therefore, rendering their glut max muscles less activated than they should be. Completing specific hip stability exercises will allow glut max to be activated and used in the key hip stability role it should be performing.

When activating a muscle, you can complete one to two sets of six to ten repetitions of each exercise but with five- to ten-second holds.

Developing hip muscle strength

Muscle strength follows the activation of hip stability muscles. Strength training has been shown to improve running economy.[8] The contact time and reflexes that control the neuromuscular system are improved through strength training. For example, strength training helps muscles of a runner's legs 'pre-activate' before the runner lands.

This pre-activation of the muscles increases the stiffness of the leg and joints ahead of landing. The stiffer muscles in the runner's leg not only absorb more shock from the impact ground reaction forces on landing, but also help the muscle-tendon units store more energy. The greater the energy stored on landing, the greater the propulsion will be when the tendon recoils and 'springs' the runner forwards (see chapter 6, 'Run with great technique', for more on utilising your natural springs).

When strengthening a hip stability muscle, complete three sets of 12 to 15 repetitions of each exercise.

Developing hip muscle endurance

The third stage of muscle training for maximising a runner's hip stability is building muscular endurance. We all have a concept of endurance – that is, doing things for a long time without succumbing to fatigue. In the context of hip stability muscle endurance for runners, this means that the muscles required for hip stability can generate enough force production repeatedly in order to absorb the repetitive loads from the impact of landing.

Running consists of repetitive muscle contractions that unavoidably subject the body to various levels of fatigue. Don't forget that a runner running for one hour running at a cadence of 90 steps/min will require enough muscular endurance of the hip stability muscles to contract forcibly up to 5,400 times on each leg.

Research has shown that as fatigue develops over the duration of exercise, the protective mechanism of the muscle diminishes.[9] The result for runners of reduced muscular protection is an elevated injury risk.

When building endurance of hip stability muscles, complete one to three sets of 50 to 100 repetitions of each exercise – yes, up to 100 repetitions!

To stretch or to strengthen?

Runners can literally perform hundreds of exercises to improve their hip stability. Many runners have been introduced to various exercises from running colleagues, magazine articles, and increasingly on YouTube. In today's time-compressed and responsibility-laden world they also want maximum results for the least amount of time spent in getting the results.

In practice when prescribing hip stability exercises, I have observed that most runners will comply with the required exercise regime when it takes less than ten minutes per day to complete. Any longer than ten minutes, and I have found that the likelihood of the runner completing the required exercises diminishes. Having either a recreational or competitive runner avoiding their hip stability exercises because they feel that it will take them too long is pointless. Therefore an effective hip stability program needs to be short on time, but big on results.

I often get asked what a runner should do if they need to do 10 to 15 minutes of hip stability exercises in addition to a prescribed stretching program. My recommendation is to split the stretching and stability/strength exercises up – and do the strength in the morning, and the stretching in the evening. I find doing stretching-related exercises at night is better for an evening's sleep – as opposed to strenuous stability exercises, which can disrupt the runner's ability to get to sleep.

Alternatively, if splitting the stretching and strengthening exercises up is not an option, I will in most instances either: 'trim' the exercise list to the most crucial stretching and strength exercises to allow for regular completion, have the runner do stretch/stability exercises on alternate days, or advise the athlete to focus on the stability and strength work ahead of their stretching.

I often tell runners that a 'tight muscle is a weak muscle'. In other words, I find that a runner's need to recurringly stretch reduces somewhat when their hip muscles are both engaged and strong. Tightness of muscles such as the quadriceps, calves, and gluteus maximus is often due to ineffective recruitment and use of the key stability muscles around the hip. When the hip stability muscles are under-activated or insufficient in strength, other muscles (such as those just listed) need to pick up the 'slack', thereby getting overworked and over-recruited, or used. In the process, these muscles become excessively tight.

Four must-know hip stability exercises

I have come to favour the following four hip stability exercises for their efficacy and ability to get runners fast improvements in their level of hip stability. I believe that every runner needs to include these exercises into their weekly training routine.

As well as outlining these four exercises in this section, they are also able to be viewed at www.pogophysio.com.au/book-resources.

The four must-do running hip stability exercises are as follows:

1 *Single-leg bridges:* With one leg extended and one leg bent (with the foot flat on the ground), lift your hips high into the air so that a virtual straight line is formed from the ankles through the knee, and to the shoulder (see the following figure).

   Aim for three sets of 12 reps on each side. To build endurance, aim for 36 reps continuously.

2 *Fire hydrants:* Start in a kneeling position, with your hands flat on the floor – directly below your shoulders. Extend one leg out to the side, keeping the foot in line with the hips. Lift the leg up and down without the foot hitting the ground (see the following figure). Don't worry about having a slope of your body – this is normal.

Aim for three sets of 12 reps on each side. Progress to 36 repetitions continuously to build endurance.

3   *Hip external rotations:* Lay on your side on the edge of a bed or a table with the bottom leg bent and angled at 90 degrees. (You can place a pillow under the knee of the leg still on the table for support.) The bent leg is then lifted

so that the foot lifts upwards towards the ceiling (see the following figure).

Aim for 100 reps continuously on each side. While 100 repetitions may seem like a lot, remember that you are asking these very muscles to work up to 5,400 times throughout a one-hour run! To build endurance, add resistance with a resistance band.

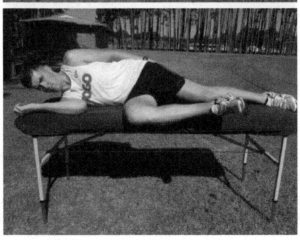

4   *Sit to stands:* Sit in a chair with your bottom positioned close to the edge of the chair and one leg extended out in front (see the following figure). Pushing up through the exercising leg aim to drive the weight of your body forwards and upwards quickly into a standing position. Lower yourself back down on the same single leg.

Progressions exist with the hands being positioned across the chest, overhead, or overhead with a dumbbell. If progressing to using a dumbbell, start with one-kilogram and build upwards in weight over time.

Aim for three sets of 12 reps on each leg. In order to build endurance, aim to complete 36 reps continuously.

How often should I do these exercises?

In practice I regularly get asked how often these hip stability exercises should be completed. The regularity with which you complete these exercises will depend on four factors. They are:

>   *The degree of your hip stability.* When hip stability is assessed (through the subjective and objective measures

covered in this chapter) as being deficient, I recommend that the runner completes the exercises as close to daily as possible.

Daily completion of the exercises will allow the runner to progress through the stages of muscle activation, strength and endurance in the shortest amount of time. I have observed significant activation and early strength gains being made by runners in as little as two to three weeks. Developing greater strength, and endurance of the hip stability muscles tends to occur between three and six weeks.

I often give runners a two-week challenge to improve their hip stability when they have sub-par scores on testing. After two weeks, the frequency of completing these exercises can often reduce to three to four times per week, providing appropriate scores are achieved at the time of retesting.

> *Your injury profile.* If you are injured or recovering from injury, daily completion of the exercises is ideal. Daily completion of the exercises will assist with building early momentum in your rehabilitation. Given that most running injuries have a significant contribution coming from hip stability deficits, anything less than daily completion will only serve to delay rehabilitation outcomes, and a return to normal running. Once the injury is under control, the frequency of completion may shift from daily completion back to several times per week.

> *Your level of training.* Just as a rehabilitating runner needs to complete hip stability exercises daily, so too will a runner in heavy training.

Quite simply, the further you intend to run, the more frequently you should aim to complete these four exercises. Heavy training may incorporate higher intensity training sessions, or greater weekly running volume. Either way, the runner in heavy training is wise to increase the frequency of their hip stability exercises in order to keep pace with the greater demands being placed on their body.

For example, a runner aiming to complete an upcoming marathon should aim for daily completion of these exercises, whereas a runner aiming to complete a 5 or 10 kilometre event may complete the exercises two to three times per week.

> *Your motivation and desire to experience pain and injury-free, and faster running.* The more motivated you are, the more likely you will be to get these exercises completed. Simple.

A maxim that I regularly share in practice with my clients is that when it comes to hip stability exercises 'consistency beats frequency'. What I mean by this is, it is of little benefit for a runner to be initially enthused about completing their hip stability exercises, only to then not follow through beyond one or two weeks of frequent completion.

Before we progress to the fifth and final step of discovering how to run pain and injury free, don't forget to study the hip movements and stability of the elite runners whenever and wherever possible. Watch footage of any of the great or elite runners and do an inventory of what you notice about the way that they move. Typically, you will observe that when they run, very little movement of their trunk or excessive movements of their hips or pelvis occurs.

Keep in mind my analogy from chapter 6 of a runner looking like they are a 'box' on legs. That is, their top half barely moves while their legs 'cycle' around in a motion similar to a cycling pedal stroke. The elite runners make it look impossibly easy, but be encouraged and inspired by the grace of their smooth movement!

As runners, we all need something to aspire to. Even if you do not become the next Olympic champion you will still be well and truly on your way to running to your fullest potential by addressing your hip stability though this, the fourth step.

After a check of the chapter key points, you are now ready to move onto the fifth and final step of running pain free and faster – understanding the power of rest.

Step 4: The importance of hip stability – key points

> Hip stability is a subset of core stability. Hip stability pertains to the degree of support that the muscles around the hip and pelvis provide, when a runner makes contact with the ground on single-leg landing.

> Several key muscles stabilise three key movements around the hips: sideways or lateral movement, extension, and external rotation of the hips.

> Running is a single-leg sport. A runner bounds from one single leg to the other. Over the course of one hour of running, a runner may land on each leg up to 5,400 times! Hip stability is therefore crucial due to the loads associated with the repetitive motion of running.

> Hip stability is important because it will markedly reduce the risk of a runner developing a running-related injury. A full rehabilitation and recovery from injury will ensue if hip instability as a contributing factor in injury onset is appropriately addressed.

> Hip stability is also important in potentiating faster running speeds and greater running economy, as a runner with stable hips wastes less energy and loses less time, compared to a runner whose hips collapse on landing.

Step 5: The importance of hip stability – key points (continued)

> All running injuries should be assessed using a 'hip down and foot up' approach. Failure to do so may result in an injury rehabilitation program that does not address all contributing injury factors.

> As a runner gets fatigued, hip stability will tend to worsen, with the degree of hip collapsing becoming more evident. This will increase loading on the runner's legs and also slow the runner down.

> Subjective and objective measures can be used to assess a runner's hip stability. In order to best assess hip stability, a combination of both is best. It is a good idea to consult with a health professional where possible in order to get accurate objective testing performed.

> Four must-do hip stability exercises will benefit all runners. Frequency of completion of these exercises will depend on several factors: injury profile, distances covered in training and racing, and the degree of hip stability deficit that was detected intially through testing.

> When it comes to hip stability exercise completion, consistency of completion is more important than frequency of completion.

Case study: Chris

Chris presented in my practice just six weeks before a major 10-kilometre road race. Chris was an up and coming junior elite triathlete who was referred to see me by his triathlon coach, for body maintenance and performance optimisation.

I performed a complete triathlon screening (running screening with additional tests to determine body attributes necessary for efficient swimming and cycling). On objective testing of Chris's hip stability, Chris had just 15 degrees of hip external rotation, of both his right and left legs – a long way from the 40 degrees that constitute a 'pass mark' for sufficient hip external rotation. Chris' single-leg squat test, single-leg bridge hold test, and side bridge hold test scores were also well below par for what an aspiring professional athlete should ideally score.

Specific strengthening exercises were prescribed for Chris in order to address his marked hip stability deficits. In the final week leading into the event, I retested Chris, and his results showed his hip external rotation range had improved, and now easily surpassed 40 degrees on both legs.

One week after re-testing, Chris went on to record a PB by just over one minute in the 10-kilometre event. This placed Chris third in a class field of elite runners. Chris posted a lightning fast 30 minute and 30 second 10-kilometre time.

Case study: Chris (continued)

While not all of Chris' result could directly be attributed to the improvements he made in his hip external rotation, I believe a large part of Chris' PB and success was due to Chris running with improved running economy due to having greatly improved his hip stability.

Chapter 9

STEP 5: The power of rest

Step 1: Discover your running body

Step 2: Run with great technique

Step 3: Navigate the footwear maze

Step 4: The importance of hip stability

Step 5: The power of rest

The fifth and final step to running pain and injury free and faster is all too often overlooked by runners of all levels. Many runners know that they should do it more often, yet then feel bad when they finally do it. I'm referring to most runners' struggle, and often times sheer inability, to take a 'day off' – or to schedule a 'rest session'.

The majority of runners find it incredibly difficult to take a day or even a single training session off from their training. They fear losing fitness and hard-earned physical conditioning as a result of not training.

A runner who is forced to stop running for any length of time is normally very reluctant to do so and will often develop withdrawal symptoms. The runner (or the runner's spouse) will immediately commence searching for anything that will allow the runner back to their much loved running training!

The very thought of not running for a day or several days in a row, or perhaps sticking to a very easy recovery training run, can create unfounded fears and anxieties in the minds of many runners.

Yet, ironically, taking a day off from training is an imperative step in the quest of any runner who is legitimately looking to run both faster and injury free. As a runner, you can only ignore rest for so long before the results of not scheduling it will catch up with you.

If a little is good, more must be better

If you're targeting a specific running goal, you tend to spend considerable time in training testing yourself and pushing your limits, training frequently and with a 'hard' intensity. With a running event looming, most runners in training are all too aware of the fact that they 'only have *x* amount of weeks' until the event.

Your experience with training will normally lead you to draw the conclusion that more running (greater distance and frequency) tends to correspond with improved performance. So the default training maxim or mindset becomes 'if a little is good, more training must be better'.

However, the adoption of this mindset can quickly become problematic. While this mindset will hold true for a large bulk of training, at a certain point the 'put in and get it out' relationship of training to performance no longer exists as a 1:1 ratio. Let me explain.

The body has in-built repair mechanisms that track the damage that training produces in the body. The mantra of 'if a little is good, more must be better' holds true when the repair mechanisms can keep pace with the micro damage that training produces within the body. Often the beginner runner will be able to build, and build, with their training, with no obvious damage to the body being accrued. This makes the runner feel like an almost endless degree of increase in training is possible.

However, for both the beginner and the seasoned runner – who are both pushing hard in training, seeking fitness and performance gains – a threshold of 'too much' training will eventually be crossed if the training program continues to increase in distance and/or intensity.

This threshold is crossed when doing more frequent or intense training no longer correlates with better running performance. In other words, input or effort is not reflected by the output in the performance that follows.

When this mismatch of input and output occurs, the runner can very easily become discouraged and disappointed. At an extreme, the runner who has trained very 'hard' and then underperforms relative to their expectation may even become quite disillusioned.

When input no longer equals output, many runners begin to look for factors that may have contributed to their lacklustre, or less than expected performance. The under-performing runner will often consider everything and anything else as a possible cause for their under-performance, before they consider that they may in fact be over-training, as a result of not factoring enough rest into their training program. The concept of not scheduling enough rest is many times completely overlooked by the under-performing runner.

A common run coaching axiom is to remind runners to not run their fast runs too slow and their recovery runs too fast! Many runners will get this wrong in training – instead racing in what should be steady or recovery runs and later not having enough 'zip' to put into what should be their faster training sessions. Not running slow enough on easy days is an extremely common error that many runners make. Turning down the pace on a designated recovery training run seems logical as a concept, yet in practice for runners it can be extremely difficult.

In order to truly experience injury-free and faster running you cannot afford to overlook the power of rest. Appropriate rest must be factored into a training program.

In *Lore of Running*, renowned medical doctor and exercise physiologist Dr Tim Noakes sums up the need for caution and adherence to rest by quoting Arthur Newton (a remarkable ultra-marathoner whose career spanned from 1922 to 1935): 'perhaps one of the chief points is to regulate your training so as to be sure of always being on the safe side: even the least sign of overdose will surely lead to trouble'.

Not just a rookie error

I believe scheduling rest is one of the most underestimated and, often times, sadly ignored concepts when it comes to running training. The power of 'rest' is little appreciated by many athletes, and it's not just recreational runners who fail to schedule and take appropriate rest.

Overlooking the importance of rest is an oversight that recreational runners through to the ranks of elite runners are often guilty of. Over my years as a physiotherapist, I have observed countless examples where the temptation of training harder instead of resting for a runner has resulted in injury development. What follows are the feelings of frustration and at times 'devastation' that accompany being sidelined and unable to compete or train.

On any given Olympic year, media reports of high-profile athletes developing injuries in the lead up to a major sporting event are common. In most of these cases, a failure to adequately rest will contribute in some way to the development of the athlete's injury. In fact, I believe that most running injuries at an elite level have 'over-training' as one of the contributing factors of the injury development process. Given that even the elite runners and athletes are prone to ignore or under 'value' the power of rest, this makes it very likely that recreational runners may also suffer the same affliction.

I observe recreational runners finding it difficult to schedule and stick to a designated rest session or complete rest day. Sadly, their failure to take a day off when needed often jeopardises their ability to compete in the very event they have been so diligently training and preparing for.

Rest and training stress

To better understand the power of rest we need to first understand the relationship between rest and the 'stress effect' that training produces. This relationship is a very delicate interplay. If a runner gets this relationship right, performance gains will result; if they get the relationship wrong, performance deficits and injuries will likely result.

In simple terms, any run training session will 'stress' the body, resulting in micro-damage to the body's structural elements. So every time we run, our tissues (bones, ligaments, tendons, muscles, and connective tissues) succumb to micro-trauma from the stress of the exercise. This damage also includes damage to blood vessels (from impact) which can result in blood marker, hormone, and even cardiac alterations.

Exercise has been found to initiate both metabolic and mechanical events that can damage muscle tissue and lead to soreness. The metabolic factors include 'microscopic' events that occur within our cells.

For example, the high body temperature produced through running may disrupt muscle protein structures and increase free radical production. Free radicals are molecules that are produced through exercise, which can lead to cell damage and the premature ageing of cells. While these events are not visible to the human eye, they initiate muscle injury.

Although this damage isn't always apparent immediately after exercise, scientists believe that these changes continue well into the period following exercise. So even after you have stopped running, the tissues are experiencing disruption for many days following a hard training session!

However, don't despair, as it is not all bad news.

Repairing the damage

While such 'damage' may seem dire, the good news is that the body has a miraculous array of invisible repair mechanisms working at all times for our benefit. These repair processes and mechanisms happen automatically – they do not need to be 'turned on' or even 'switched off'. They work efficiently during the day, but in the evening when we are sleeping, the body's repair mechanisms go into overdrive.

Ordinarily with training, the stress from the training load exceeds the repair that occurs during rest for several consecutive days. The body then adapts to the training stimulus via its self-repair mechanisms and, in doing so, becomes 'fitter' and stronger.

It is this continual cycle of overloading the body with the stress of training, followed by adequate rest and repair, which over time leads to improved fitness and performance.

The taper – a case of letting rest work for you

When a runner is in the final weeks of event preparation, they will often reduce their training volume, and/or training intensity. This is done with the intention of 'freshening up' for the race. Such a structured and strategic reduction is known as a 'taper'. The taper process is an example of how a stressed body, when given rest sessions, will enter into a state of 'freshness'. The runner will generally then go on to perform at their optimal level following the taper. At a very minimum the runner will normally perform better than what would have likely been achieved in a fatigued or unrested state, had a taper not occurred.

No set formula exists for tapering for running events. Getting this balance correct is not easy. In fact, many runners tinker with their race tapers over many years. As a general rule, the longer the distance of an upcoming event, the greater the volume reduction and reduction in training intensity that is required as part of the taper. A longer time frame for the reduction in training is also required for longer distance events, such as preparing for a marathon. For example, a short 5- to 10-kilometre race may only require a one- to two-day taper, while a marathon may require a taper up to four weeks long.

Every runner will approach a race taper slightly differently. Some will not do one at all. Others will prepare fastidiously and reduce running volume in a very mathematical and precise way. Getting a taper 'right' can be a lifelong quest for runners and athletes at large. It's similar to the golfer (recreational or professional) seeking to play the perfect round of golf! Such is the pursuit of the perfect taper.

I suggest that you experiment with reducing your running training leading into events and discover what preparation and taper leaves you feeling the best on race day. Over the years I have tried many different tapers, for events of all different distances – ranging from 5 kilometres to the full marathon. Even after running many road races of a multitude of distances I remain unsure of my ideal, or 'perfect', taper. However, I will give you some general guidelines that I follow.

These guidelines for tapering for different distance running events are as follows:

> *5-kilometre event:* A taper is generally not needed. You are quite safe to follow your normal training routine in the week(s) leading into a 5-kilometre event. The only reason you may need a taper is if the race is your main event for the season. In this case you would be wise to reduce your training volume several days out from the race. This will help your legs to 'freshen up'.

> *10-kilometre event:* Try reducing your running volume by 20 to 30 per cent in the week leading into the race. I recommend still leaving some shorter than normal hard runs and efforts as part of your program.

> *Half-marathon (21.1-kilometre):* I suggest reducing your volume by 20 per cent two weeks out, and then by 30 per cent over the last week leading into the event.

Keeping some efforts in your program two weeks out is worthwhile, but reduce the number of harder sessions or efforts in the week leading into the event.

> *Marathon (42.2-kilometre):* I suggest reducing your running volume by 20, 30, and 50 per cent over the three weeks leading into the event. I believe that many runners (including myself) do far too much training during the last several weeks leading into a marathon. Many times, a runner can become anxious that they have not done enough training in the lead-up to a marathon – and this can occur whether it is their first marathon or they have done several. As a result, they will often 'cram' training into the last several weeks, which ultimately leaves them feeling flat, tired and less than their best on race day.

Generally, in the immediate two weeks leading into the race, there is no great need to continue with too much speed work in training. However, some runners find that continuing to include some short and sharp running efforts helps them – even if this is more psychologically beneficial than being physiologically beneficial. Every runner responds differently to tapers, which is why you will need to experiment a little to find your best taper routine(s).

Overuse running injuries

When the tissue damage accrued by your body due to repetitive training begins to outpace your body's tissue repair mechanisms, you are on the way to developing an injury. Just as the name suggests, these injuries are due to repetitive use (overuse) and strain in tissues. Failing to rest – whether it be not getting enough sleep or not scheduling a break from your training – can significantly increase the likelihood of you developing an overuse running injury.

Overuse running injuries differ from 'acute injuries'. Acute injuries are the injuries that occur quickly or happen 'out of nowhere', and include such injuries as calf, quadriceps, or hamstring muscle tears. Sprained ankles are another example. These injuries involve a sudden one-off large force or load that damages the body's tissues. This is in contrast to an overuse injury, where the body is exposed to repetitive loads over time that result in a gradual onset of injury.

For a runner, if steps one to four of the five step method to running injury free and faster are in place (refer to chapters 5 to 8), the repetitiveness of the running motion and the associated strain of training will generally only become an issue when the runner neglects rest. When rest is neglected, the body's repair mechanisms don't keep pace with the training stress being placed on the body. A mismatch between stress and rest is now at play within the body.

In runners, overuse injuries can affect any tissue of the lower limbs. Bone is particularly susceptible to repeated stress and overuse injuries, with common bony injuries including: shin pain (splints), stress fractures of the foot bones, and stress reactions of any lower limb bone (foot, shin, or hips). Other common overuse running injuries that typically have inadequate rest as one of the key contributory factors for injury development include: ITB friction syndrome, Achilles tendon injuries, and patella-femoral (knee cap) pain. If regular and appropriate rest sessions are scheduled, the risk of developing these running injuries decreases dramatically.

Common training errors

Failing to schedule and stick to rest is very problematic. You may 'get away with it' for several days, weeks or even months. However, flirt with not taking a rest session for long enough and, with the passage of time, you are almost guaranteed to develop an injury.

Failure to schedule rest or adhere to a rest session may be defined as a 'training error'. As the term suggests, it's an error or misjudgement made in the runner's training schedule. The error may relate to the scheduling of rest, adhering to rest days or sessions, or errors made in training volume, intensity or frequency.

I have observed that training errors play a part in the development of the vast majority of overuse running injuries. I regularly observe injured runners who, when their pre-injury training history is chronicled, have had a recent sudden increase in running training volume, frequency and/or intensity. Alternatively, the frequency, volume and intensity of their training has not changed but they have neglected for whatever reason to schedule appropriate and well-timed rest sessions.

This is often the case with the development of the seven most common running injuries we looked at in chapter 4.

I see runners making five common training errors. These errors, along with how they can contribute to injury development are as follows:

1 *Failing to schedule a rest day or rest session.* The temptation to do more to get more is often intoxicating for runners. Many runners are literally 'addicted' to the positive feelings that running produces. Runners can literally experience withdrawal signs from not running due to not experiencing their routine hit of 'endorphins' and other happy hormones (such as serotonin) that they would usually experience in full and uninterrupted training.

   Endorphins are substances that the body's central nervous system and pituitary gland produce. The term *endorphin* means 'morphine like substance'. Hence, endorphins' role is to block pain that the body experiences. When a runner trains they routinely experience positive happy hormone effects and their 'pain' can be blocked by endorphins. It can be addictive!

   Not running for even a single day can, therefore, be a challenge for many runners.

2 *Doing too much too soon.* This can be a pitfall of the over-zealous beginner runner who just wants run 'more and more'. It can likewise be the pitfall of the eager runner returning from an enforced break due to injury. For example, a beginner runner that builds up the duration (and distance) of their training sessions too quickly. Alternately, an experienced runner may increase the

overall weekly volume of their training too quickly, from one week to the next in preparation for a major event.

3   *Going too hard on consecutive training sessions.* Not every training session needs to be an intense workout. Runners must learn to discipline themselves in varying the pace and intensity across different training sessions. Many times the excitement of training takes hold and common sense and patience are erroneously forgotten. The result is that every training session ends up hard and intense. This can be a trap runners fall into when they train in a group or with others. Unfortunately, when training with groups, the temptation is ever present to begin racing with your training partners. Proceed with caution!

4   *Replacing what should be a rest session with a training session.* This often occurs when a runner is feeling 'fit' and highly motivated. I'm personally a sucker for this one. If I have had a good race or run at a Sunday event, rather than rest on the Monday morning I can be tempted to get up and run a moderate length run (often at too fast of a pace) still 'high' on the endorphins of the good race from the day before. After competing in a running event or race, even if you do not feel like you need a rest – take one.

This will allow your body sufficient time to recover.

The same principle holds true during training blocks where you get on a 'roll' and feel like you can run fast every single training run with seemingly no consequences. Be very careful when this happens. Discipline yourself to still run slowly on a recovery run, fight the temptation to turn what should be a recovery run into another hard run, and most certainly don't miss rest days.

5   *Introducing hill running into a training program.* Problems occur when hills are introduced into a running training program too quickly, or in too great of a volume or frequency. The inclines and declines associated with hills add greater load to the body's tissues. A good training program will factor in training that is completed on hills and will make allowances for appropriate recovery after hill running.

For example, running uphill is often an irritating factor for an Achilles tendon, because the uphill movement increases compression of the Achilles tendon, which can create irritation of the tendon and surrounding tissues and subsequently produce pain. A well-structured training program will allow sufficient recovery time before the runner tackles hills again in order to decrease the risk of developing an Achilles tendon injury. For the runner accustomed to hill running, this may be in two days; while for the unaccustomed hill runner, it may require four to five days to adequately recover.

Simply being aware of these five commonly made training errors will go a long way in helping you to avoid them, before going on to enjoying injury-free and faster running.

The art and science of training

The interplay of rest and the stress of training has two outcomes, depending on the balance that is struck. A runner will either experience performance gains (through getting enough rest), or the development of an injury or over-trained state (not enough rest).

This can be summarised as follows:

1   If you can get the ratio of rest to training correct, you will get performance gains.

2   If you get the rest-to-training ratio wrong, the body will eventually reach either a state of over-training or overuse injury development.

Getting this rest-to-work ratio correct is largely the 'art' part of the 'science and art' of training. The following figures depict the balance that must exist within the training cycle to avoid the runner developing painful injuries.

The training to rest see-saw

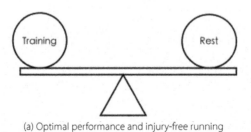

(a) Optimal performance and injury-free running

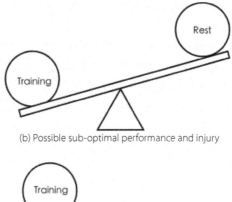

(b) Possible sub-optimal performance and injury

(c) Injury-free running but sub-optimal performance

To the limit – the over-trained runner

In addition to a heightened injury risk, the runner who fails to schedule rest sessions can be heading for another kind of trouble. Many runners assume that pushing harder in training is a sure-fire route to running success. This mindset is not surprising given runners' inherent work ethic, motivation and in some cases, their obsession.

Constantly pushing hard in training without adequate rest is actually a sure-fire route to failure and the development of an over-trained state. Among runners this is often colloquially referred to as becoming 'burnt out', 'cooked' or 'fried'. Interestingly each of these phrases relates to fire but there is to my knowledge no symbolism.

The over-trained state is the last stop on the continuum of training and rest. It can be depicted as follows:

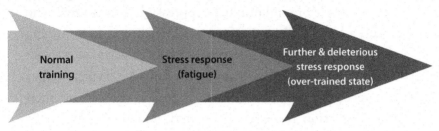

In training a runner will progress through healthy and safe (normal) training where rest and training stressors are counterbalanced, and fitness and subsequent performance improves. However, when the stress on the body begins to outpace the rest and repair mechanisms of the body, fatigue results.

If the training load continues to outpace and in effect overpower the body's ability to recover from the training load for a long enough period of time, the fatigue can escalate to a point where the runner will experience severe fatigue. This severe fatigue is synonymous with other signs of the over-trained state. For a runner, arriving at this state is serious. When this occurs the body's capacity to adapt to the stressors of training are impaired, and according to science the defence mechanisms intended to prevent death are actually initiated!

One commonly recognised sign of over-training is a depressed immune system. In medicine, this is referred to as 'immunosuppression' of the immune system. Just as with the continuum of an over-trained state, immunosuppression also exists on a scale or continuum. When a runner is mildly immunosuppressed, the runner may experience an additional head cold or two. At the extreme end of immunosuppression, the runner may find it difficult to recover from a mere benign 'bug'.

An example of mild immunosuppression is the runner who picks up a head cold in the final week leading into a running event. Many runners will question why they always seem to get sick in the final week before an important race. Typically they fail to recognise that their bodies are over-trained and their immune function has been hampered, and they are actually immunosuppressed.

The signs and symptoms of over-training can be classified into physiological, psychological, immunological and biochemical signs and symptoms. They are summarised in the following table.

Signs of over-training

Physiological	Psychological	Immunological	Biochemical
Decreased training performance. For example, it is more difficult than usual to hold certain training paces or times	Feeling a bit 'down' emotionally	Experiencing more head (upper respiratory) colds, flus and illnesses	Potential anaemia (loss of red blood cells from repeated foot striking)

Physiological	Psychological	Immunological	Biochemical
An elevated resting heart rate	Not experiencing the same 'high' after training or in life in general	Unable to 'shake' benign (low-grade) illnesses	Elevated cortisol levels (stress hormone)
Feeling lethargic and fatigued more than unusual, for no apparent reason	Feeling greater levels of anxiety than usual	Increased susceptibility to chronic illness	Reduced male and female sex hormones (testosterone and oestrogen)
Disruption of the normal menstrual cycle for female runners	Reduced libido	Reduced healing of body tissues; for example, muscle, bone and wounds	Reduced thyroid hormone function
Greater rate of injury development and a lowered resilience to injury	Loss of interest and enjoyment with training or competing	Increased susceptibility to bruising	Increased acidity in the blood and tissues

Sleep easy

Sleep is a key component of a runner getting sufficient rest and maximising their body's repair mechanisms. Sadly, most runners – along with the general population – do not get enough quality sleep.

Many people live in a state of unrecognised sleep deprivation. In the US, 50 to 70 million people were found to be on the brink of physical and mental collapse because of fatigue.[1] According to a 2005 Gallup Poll in the US, the average sleep duration reported was 6.8 hours during the week and 7.4 hours on the weekend.

In 2014, *Sports Physio* magazine reported that the unpublished results of clinical tests being performed (at the Australian Institute of Sport) on elite athletes demonstrated poor sleep quality and habits. Athletes' sleep patterns and wake cycles were monitored using wrist activity monitors and sleep diaries. On average, athletes across all investigated sports obtained a total sleep time of six hours and seven minutes, well below the recommended seven to nine hours per night.

What is quality sleep?

For most adults the recommended sleep amount for sufficient repair processes is seven to nine hours.[2] Most people will find eight hours of sleep perfect. Any less and you may feel sleepy and drowsy throughout your day; any more and you may feel unnaturally sluggish. But it is not just the volume of sleep that matters – the quality or 'depth' of sleep, and the number of sleep cycles you go through, are also of importance.

Most people experience five to six sleep cycles during a normal night's sleep. Each sleep cycle is comprised of two parts that will each last between 60 and 90 minutes. The first part of a sleep cycle is broken down into four stages, with stages three and four being the most restful part of sleep.[3] The second part of the sleep cycle is when dreaming occurs and this is well known as REM (rapid eye movement) sleep. Typically, only a few minutes of the first 90 minute cycle are spent in REM sleep. However, with each successive sleep cycle, REM sleep progressively takes up more of the ninety minute sleep cycle.

Elderly and middle-age people tend to spend less time in deep sleep than younger people. The elderly tend to secrete lesser amounts of certain chemicals that regulate sleep and wake cycles, and also wake up much more frequently than younger people. As people mature in years, sleep can become more shallow, broken and variable in duration.

Ideally, our sleep should be relatively undisturbed. For example, regular toilet trips, a snoring partner, a pet in the bed or too much alcohol or caffeine in your body can all cause deleterious sleep disruptions!

Waking up feeling unrefreshed, falling asleep during the day (particularly in darkened rooms), difficulty in maintaining energy levels, and experiencing sugar cravings can all be signs that you may not be getting enough sleep.

Why is sleep important?

During sleep, important hormones are released and regulated; one of these is growth hormone. Growth hormone causes children to grow, regulates muscle mass, regulates the repair of muscle tissue, and controls the distribution of fat in adults. When you do not get enough sleep, the function of growth hormone is disrupted.

Growth hormone is released during REM sleep. In order to go into REM sleep, you need to ensure that you are asleep for a long enough period of time. As noted previously, most athletes and the population at large do not get enough sleep, and therefore do not receive the required full and complete cycles of sleep.

Another important hormone that is released when we sleep is leptin. Leptin directly influences appetite and controls body weight by alerting the body when it is 'full'.[4] A runner who doesn't have enough of this regulating hormone because of sleep deprivation may have an insatiable appetite that may lead to subsequent weight gain.

Receiving adequate sleep also helps to reduce the levels of cortisol (the 'stress' hormone) in the body. When cortisol levels are high, neurotransmitter balance in the brain can be disrupted. This disruption may cause mental disturbances such as heightened irritability, anxiety, insomnia, and even depression. The good news is that sufficient sleep helps to reduce cortisol levels.[5]

Recently, evidence has emerged showing the negative effect that sleep deprivation has on our bone health. Healthy bones are necessary for a healthy life. One of the chief bone problems people may encounter in life is the development of osteoporosis. An interesting study of 1,146 participants found that sleep-deprived women who had less than six and a half hours of sleep per night had lower BMD scores compared with women who received adequate sleep.[6] These results were supported by another study that looked at 602 Chinese women aged between 18 and 80 years, which found the same negative association between inadequate amounts of sleep and BMD. Compared to those who slept eight hours, individuals who slept five hours or less had significantly lower total BMD.[7]

Sleep has also been found to slow the ageing process, boost the immune system, and improve brain function. Dr Don Colbert in *Seven Pillars of Health* states that 'good sleep is one of the best health principles available; yet sadly very few people get enough sleep, which degrades and even ruins health'.

Tips to maximise your sleep quality

Here are some ways you can increase the amount of sleep you get and importantly also improve the quality of your sleep:

> Reduce exposure to electronic device screen time 30 minutes before bed (this includes TV, computers, tablets, and phones). These devices 'feed' your eyes with light. We are designed to hormonally fall into sync with the rhythms of nature – so when the sun goes down, for example, so should we.

Normally, when the light fades you get a release of the hormone melatonin into your bloodstream. Melatonin's function is to make you drowsy. By viewing electronic screens in the evening, your body's in-built mechanism to make you sleepy and have you enter into quality sleep is blocked.

> Avoid caffeine at least three hours before bed. Some health scientists believe that caffeine intake should be limited beyond midday.

> Avoid 'revving up' your body with exercise within three hours of bedtime.

> Aim to eat a modest and nutritious dinner four hours before bedtime. A well-timed and nutritious meal helps to stabilise your blood sugar levels throughout the night.

> Establish your body clock by keeping a consistent routine for going to bed and also waking up.

> Restrict fluid intake past 5 pm to reduce excessive night-time toilet trips.

> Keep the bedroom cool, dark and quiet and at a comfortable temperature (18 to 22° is ideal).

> Turn down the household's lights and reduce exposure to bright lights 30 to 60 minutes before bed. Again, this is because bright light disturbs our normal hormonal responses at night that would normally prepare us for sleep.

> Keep the bedroom for sleeping – avoid taking work to bed. No laptops or to-do lists!

> Remove TVs from your bedroom. If there is no TV, there is no temptation. TVs can be traps that delay you getting to sleep and also sources of light.

Avoiding over-training and injury – example programs

So far in this chapter we have established the need to both schedule and take rest in order to run injury free and unlock your full running potential.

In the following table, I have outlined some guidelines of when and how to schedule rest into running programs. The table is broken into example programs for beginner (B), intermediate (I) and advanced (A) runners. The table is further broken down into training guidelines for three popular event distances: 10 kilometre, half marathon, and the full marathon.

Please note that this table constitutes general advice only. If you require greater detail, I recommend consulting with a qualified running coach, or even a veteran or experienced runner.

	Level of runner	Typical weekly volume (kms)	Number of rest days in a month
10 km	B	10–20	15 (every second day)
	I	20–40	8 (every fourth day)
	A	40–80	4 (once per week)
Half marathon	B	25–35	12
	I	35–55	6
	A	55–90	4

	Level of runner	Typical weekly volume (kms)	Number of rest days in a month
Marathon	**B**	40–60	10
	I	50–70	6
	A	70–100+	4

Knowing when to run and when to rest

One of the most frequently asked questions I get from runners suffering from niggles and injuries is, 'Should I run or should I rest?' My response is typically 'It depends'. In giving a considered and professional response I need to take many factors into consideration. My ability to give appropriate advice has been formulated through years of both personal, and clinical experience.

The problem for most injured, or niggle-carrying, runners is that they do not have the experience of a trained health professional to draw upon, in order to make an informed and wise decision. Instead they rely on their own 'gut instinct' or intuition, research on Google, what their running friends tell them to do, or what their family suggests that they do! As a result, the injured runner will often make an erroneous and misguided decision about whether they should run or rest.

The consequence of these misguided decisions is often the pain of a worsening injury, and the frustration that results from being side-lined and unable to train.

A recent study published in the *Australian Journal of Physiotherapy* revealed that a staggering number of runners continue to train and compete while suffering from overuse injuries.[8] Over 1,000 runners were surveyed across five different recreational running events (5 to 10 kilometres) in order to determine the prevalence of injuries immediately before a race. Of the respondents, 227 (22 per cent) reported musculoskeletal pain (injury) before the race. When broken down by gender it was found that the prevalence of pain was 20 per cent among the 796 male respondents, and 27 per cent among the 253 female respondents. Simply put, this equates to an average of one in five runners participating in recreational running events while suffering from an overuse injury.

Furthermore the study found that the average time course of experiencing symptoms related to the injury was 30 days. Therefore the runners had been experiencing pain for approximately one month and yet they still chose to compete with the injury or pain.

The most common sites of injuries found in the study (in order of most to least prevalent) were the knee, foot, ankle, spine, and the hip.

The results of this study highlight one of two things:

> The runners were choosing to run 'through' the pain, or

> The runners were ill-equipped to decide whether they should rest or compete, likely due to a lack of knowledge about how to best manage the pain that they were experiencing.

With even a small level of insight and knowledge about injury management, I believe that many recreational runners can significantly reduce the likelihood of developing an injury. They can avoid what starts out to be a low-level pain or niggle developing into a full-blown and nasty overuse running injury.

In order to make wise decisions when you find yourself unsure about whether to run or rest, you need to be able to identify the *severity and pattern* of the pain you are experiencing. Establishing this information will provide you with insights into what the pain or niggle you are experiencing actually 'means'. Many injuries could be lessened or even avoided if the runner was equipped with the appropriate knowledge about what their pain means. Poorly informed decisions as to whether to train or rest are made when a runner lacks knowledge.

Identifying the severity and pattern of the pain from your injury can also guide you in how careful you need to be with your training, and how disciplined you need to be about resting. I believe this information is of importance to all runners.

Let's explore how to determine whether to run or to rest.

What is your pain trying to tell you?

The following considerations need to be taken into account when you are trying to decide whether to run or rest. These patterns will help you determine both the severity, and the nature of your pain. Armed with this knowledge you will be in a position to make an informed decision to either train or to rest. Subsequently, you will lessen the likelihood of making an ill-informed or misguided decision about your training.

The following seven considerations will also alert you as to whether you need to seek medical services.

Consideration 1: What is the overall 'trend' of your pain?

You need to determine whether your pain is getting worse, staying the same, or getting better. Working this out will determine your course of action as follows:

> If the pain is *worsening*, it is wise to seek professional medical assistance. Doing the same thing in training will not curb the pain but will only lead to further exacerbation of your pain, which will result in longer recovery and rehabilitation time frames. Pain that is worsening is a clear indicator that if you keep doing the same things, you are likely headed for trouble.

> Pain that is *staying the same* (that is, not worsening or getting better) typically will also need medical attention – for example, a consultation with a physiotherapist. As a general guide, the longer you run with pain, pushing through it and 'putting up' with it, the longer it will take until you are able to return to running pain free.

On average, it will take you the equivalent number of weeks or months (or even years) that you have carried an injury for, to return to fully functional pain-free running. For example, if you ran with Achilles pain for 16 weeks, it may take you up to 16 weeks before you can run pain free (with the assistance of an appropriate injury rehabilitation program). Please note that this injury-to-recovery ratio is a guide only, because it is possible to reduce injury rehabilitation times with appropriate interventions and a structured and well-guided return to training.

> If the injury is *improving*, you may or may not need medical help (rehabilitation). Runners are often unsure of whether this type of injury requires assessment and treatment from a health professional. I encourage runners who have carried a low-grade 'niggle' for greater than two weeks, to be assessed by a health professional such as a physiotherapist. This guideline applies even if your injury is slowly improving and the pain is subsiding. The rationale here is that by letting the pain settle on its own, the underlying contributory factors that produced the pain in the first instance are yet to be addressed. If you return to training without having addressed these contributing factors, you are at risk of the injury returning and producing another cycle of pain, injury and frustration.

Consideration 2: Does your pain get worse when you run?

If your pain worsens with running, reducing your training frequency and/or your training volume will normally be necessary. If the pain experienced is proportionate to the amount of training being done, it is a sign that running more, and not resting, will only serve to worsen the pain. Further running will also prolong the recovery time.

In clinical practice, pain that increases with activity is referred to as 'mechanical' or 'movement-generated' pain. With mechanical pain, the degree of pain is proportionate to the amount of movement being performed.

An example would be the runner with a sore big toe who doesn't have too much trouble or pain when resting; however, when the runner completes a 30-minute run, they return home hobbling because the big toe pain has worsened. The pain worsened because the mechanics of running (pushing off with the big toe) created strain and subsequent pain in the injured structure – the big toe.

So if movement (using your body) makes your pain worse, it is likely your injury will require the intervention of a physiotherapist in order to help you make a return to injury-free running.

Consideration 3: Does your pain get worse the further you run?

In addition to identifying that your pain gets worse with running (consideration 2), it is also useful to identify if more (longer or further) running produces more pain. Pain that worsens throughout a run in proportion to the furthered duration or distance may indicate injury to bones or joints.

For example, the pain of 'shin splints' may be only slightly noticeable at the start of a run but may get substantially worse by the end of a run. Muscle injuries will tend to behave the same way and will become more painful with furthered running.

Alternately, pain that is worse before or only at the start of a training run, that then subsides as the runner gets 'warm' and starts the training session, is often consistent with tendon-specific injuries. An example of this would be patella (knee) or Achilles tendon pain, that is sore for the first five to ten minutes of running but then progressively subsides in intensity the further and longer the runner trains. Runners suffering from tendon injuries will typically express that their pain 'goes away when they warm up'.

In both instances – pain that increases during a run and pain that decreases during a run – it is important to see a health professional such as a physiotherapist in order for a diagnosis to be made and appropriate treatment to be commenced.

Consideration 4: Has your pain progressed from being present only after running, to now being present before running?

Many running injuries will initially only produce pain after a run. The runner begins the training run oblivious to pain, but by the end of the run they experience pain (consideration 2). When no rehabilitation or training modifications are in place, the injury may progress to the point where pain is now felt before a training session commences.

Such a progression of pain signifies that the injury has progressed in severity. When the pain progresses to the point where you are in significant pain even before you begin exercising this is a clear indication that the injury is serious.

In such cases, you should seek professional medical assistance regarding the appropriate diagnosis, treatment, and management of the injury. Unless training changes are implemented quickly, the pain will continue to worsen with further activity, until you become completely sidelined and unable to train.

A 'text-book' example of this type of pain 'behaviour' or progression is the development of shin splints. A runner suffering from early stage shin splints will initially experience pain only after a training run. With further running, the shin bone is subjected to further stress, and the injury to the shin bone both advances and worsens. Eventually the runner experiences pain not only after a training run, but also pain that is still present for the commencement of the next training run. This shift in pain experience signifies a worsening in severity of the shin pain.

The runner's shins are now in a state of serious overload, where even a day or so of rest is not allowing for pain to reduce. The runner who continues running on shins this sore will be likely heading towards the development of a stress fracture. A stress fracture (small fracture of the outside casing of the bone) will force the runner to stop.

To test for shin pain, I will get a runner to hop on each leg, half a dozen times, and tell me if their pain is greater than a three out of ten on a pain scale. If pain (of greater than 3/10 intensity) is present on a single-leg hop on the sore leg, I advise the runner to cease from running until such a time as they can hop on the injured leg without any pain. In cases of advanced shin pain, this may require the runner to rest and avoid the impact loading of running for up to six weeks. In less severe cases, it may require only two weeks of rest from running.

Tendon pain (for example Achilles tendon injuries) can be very slow to respond to rest and/or treatment, and can behave a little differently to bone injuries such as the preceding example of shin splints. Unlike injured bone or muscle, which tends to feel worse with further running, tendon pain can often feel worse at the start of a run but feel better by the end of a run.

However, if the tendon was touched at the end of a run it would likely be quite sensitive. The best guide for tendon pain is how the tendon responds to both touch and hopping the next morning upon getting out of bed. As a guide, if the pain the next day on rising and then while doing the single-leg hop test is greater than three out of ten, resting from running that day is wise. Then try the hop test and feel the tendon the following day – if the pain is still present it is best to seek professional help.

Consideration 5: Are you experiencing evening pain?

Pain experienced in the evening is an indication that the injury is either severe, or on its way to being severe. Pain experienced in the evening should not be ignored. There are two types of evening pain that you should be aware of in trying to decide whether to run or not, and whether receiving medical intervention is required:

> *Pain that **wakes** you up through the night.* If the pain that you are experiencing is severe, unrelenting, and wakes you from your sleep, I suggest you seek medical attention as soon as possible. Pain that is severe and that

wakes you up can indicate a problem that sits outside of the musculoskeletal domain. For example, organ-related cancers or malignancies of the spine can cause this type of intense evening pain. However, it is important to differentiate between pain that *wakes you up*, and pain that *is present when you wake up*. As an example, if you roll over in bed and your sore lower back wakes you up as you roll, this is distinct from a sore lower back that actually wakes you up.

Although it can be tricky at times to differentiate between pain that wakes you up, and pain that is present when you wake up, most people can discern the difference. Pain that wakes you up can often require urgent medical assistance.

> *Pain that is present **only** when you wake up.* This pain is present when you wake from sleep throughout the course of a night's sleep. A classic example of this is a runner with a sore Achilles tendon. The first few steps in the morning or through the night (for example when getting up for a toilet break) will often be sore. Another example may be osteoarthritis of the joints (knee, hip, ankle and foot) or plantar fascia pain (of the heel of the foot), all of which will be most noticeable upon getting out of bed for the first few steps or, in the worst cases, for up to half an hour after rising.

When you experience pain that is present when you wake up, but not waking you up in the night, you do not need to seek urgent immediate attention. However, if the pain persists it is wise to seek professional assistance.

One of the reasons that we experience pain in the evenings is because we experience a drop in our body's cortisol levels overnight. Cortisol is a hormone that is released by the body in response to stress and low blood glucose levels. Our body's cortisol levels peak at around 8 am and reach their lowest level between midnight and 4 am.[9] Cortisol has anti-inflammatory properties and, therefore, serves as a natural anti-inflammatory agent. Hence, when cortisol levels drop so too does the natural anti-inflammatory effect that it has on any inflammation present in our bodies. The result is less blocking of the inflammation and a concomitant rise in pain levels associated with inflammation of injured body tissues and structures.

Consideration 6: What is the running time required to bring on your pain?

The earlier your pain comes on during a run, the more 'irritated' the injured tissues are, and generally the worse the injury is. It is a clear sign that the injury is worsening when it takes less time with each successive run to elicit the pain during the run. The earlier the onset of the pain, the worse the injury has become.

For example, a runner suffering from knee pain (patella-femoral) may experience greater irritation of the knee cap (patella) with further running. As the runner continues to train and ignores rest, the undersurface of the knee cap becomes progressively more and more irritated. The effect of the worsening of the knee cap's condition, is that it takes less time for the pain to come on with each successive run.

If your pain has progressed to the point where it only takes five to ten minutes of running time to bring on the pain, I suggest you rest and seek the assistance of a physiotherapist in order to have your injury professionally assessed, diagnosed, and rehabilitated.

Consideration 7: Is your pain unresponsive to rest?

If you are experiencing pain that rest alone does not seem to help, choosing to not run, and seeking professional assistance is recommended. Often times having two or three days of rest by electing to not run, can allow the body to repair or fully restore tissues that are injured. In many cases, after several days of rest the runner returns to pain-free running. However, if the body does not have time to repair the injured tissue(s) and the runner continues to run through the pain, a full-blown injury may quickly ensue.

Rest often cures the acute symptoms, but like any therapy that does not aim to correct the cause of the pain, it may ultimately fail in the long term. As soon as the runner stops resting and returns to running, the injury may recur because rest alone has not addressed the contributory factors that caused the injury (refer to chapter 4).

Managing the pains and niggles

Now that you are equipped with some knowledge about what your injury is 'trying to tell you', you are now more likely to make wiser decisions with regards to whether to train or rest.

Additionally, understanding the basics of how to best manage your pain and injury will be useful.

Many times the difference between an injury that requires a long rehabilitation time, and an injury that quickly resolves, is how well the runner manages the injury in the early phases of the injury's onset.

Astute initial management can be multi-faceted but may include:

> First aid principles such as compression and elevation of the injured body part.

> Heat and topical creams. A golden rule is to never use heat on an acute injury inside the first 48 hours. Incorrectly applying heat can cause further bleeding and swelling, and therefore extend the recovery time.

> Ice to help decrease the swelling, pain and bleeding of an acute injury inside the initial 48 hours. Acute injuries may include soft tissue strains (for example calf or hamstring strains) and sprained ligaments (ankle rolls or knee injuries). Never ice for greater than 20 minutes at a time because, interestingly, this will create more bleeding around the damaged tissue.

> Use either heat or ice for overuse injuries that are not acute in nature. I advise runners beyond the first 48 hours post injury, to use whatever is the most comfortable. This will often depend on the seasons. It's never fun to put an ice pack on in winter! The 20-minute rule per application of ice still applies.

> Allowing the body and tissues adequate time to repair between sessions. This may involve cross-training to rest from running, or complete rest from all training.

> Self-treatment strategies such as tissue therapy using foam rollers, and/or trigger point therapy using massage tools, and stretching.

> Specific rehabilitation overseen by a health professional (for example, a physio, podiatrist or sports doctor). During any professional intervention, all of the contributory factors of injury onset need to be identified. For a full recovery from injury to occur, all of these contributory factors need to be addressed.

A note on pain

It is important to remember that pain is always an indicator that something is wrong. Think of pain as your 'ally' and not your 'enemy' – listen to it. If you give your pain the attention it deserves it will assist you in your quest to keep running without interruption. Pain is an in-built mechanism that alerts us to danger and its purpose is to prevent us from hurting ourselves.

Improvements in running performance are routinely sought by hard workouts. Normally, the harder the workouts the better. Yet if these hard workouts are not interspersed with adequate rest, continuing with a string of hard workouts in training will become unachievable.

Leading American endurance coach Joe Friel says it well:

> If we wish to improve, we must regularly flirt with over-training. But by paying close attention to the elements of recovery (especially rest and nutrition), and by following a structured training program, athletes can avoid over-training.

If runners schedule adequate rest sessions and take appropriate recovery days, the negative effects of over-training can be warded off, and the likelihood of developing injuries will be lessened.

The best way to avoid this pitfall is to a follow a periodised training program that schedules weekly rest and recovery days, monthly rest and recovery weeks, and yearly rest and recovery months. Such a training plan will also provide for a gradual progression in the training workload, and must fit a runner's unique characteristics such as their running experience, age, susceptibility to illness and injury, and goals.

If you are looking to structure your running program, then using the example recovery programs outlined in this chapter will be a good starting point. If you require more detailed input, engaging the services of a coach (physical or online) would be wise.

The key points for this chapter follow.

Step 5: The power of rest – key points

Here are the key points to keep in mind from this chapter:

> When it comes to training, the maxim 'if a little is good more must be better' does not hold true. Failing to schedule appropriate rest days or sessions is a sure-fire way to end up injured or possibly over-trained.

> Failing to rest is not just an error made by beginner runners. Even elite runners fall victim to the temptation to continue training hard without scheduling adequate rest.

> The interplay between rest and the stress a runner's body experiences due to training is delicate. Get the balance right and performance gains will result; get it wrong and injury or an over-trained state will may be experienced.

> Tapering for an event is an example of boosting performance through adhering to rest. A runner's ideal taper can only be discovered through a process of trial and error.

> Getting an appropriate amount and quality of sleep is a key component in maximising the power of rest. Quality sleep is critical for the health and performance of runners and athletes.

Step 5: The power of rest – key points (continued)

> In addition to failing to schedule a rest day or rest session, other 'training errors' runners can make will also increase their likelihood of developing an injury. These other training errors can include: doing too much too soon, introducing hill running into a program, replacing a rest session with a hard training session, and the scheduling of hard sessions too close together.

> Over-training is the end-stage of a training to rest continuum, whereby the runner neglects rest over a sustained period of time. Physiological, psychological, immunological and biochemical changes result from being in an over-trained state.

> Pay close attention to what your pain is 'telling you'. It will assist you in deciding whether you should run or rest on a given day, and whether you need to seek the services of a health professional such as a physiotherapist. Using the seven considerations outlined in this chapter will improve quality of the decisions that you make.

> If rest is adhered to and your pain or injury persists, seek a professional opinion and professional help.

Case study: Phil

Phil initially presented for physiotherapy seeking rehabilitation and advice for pain in the front of his right hip. Phil was a talented recreational runner who had started preparing for an upcoming local marathon in which he was aiming to run a personal best time.

As a result, Phil was completing unaccustomed volumes of weekly running training. On average, Phil had been logging 140 kilometres each week, and had been preparing in this manner for what was close to ten weeks.

Phil's hip pain had been developing and progressively worsening over the three months before he arrived at my practice. The pain had gotten so bad that by the time Phil saw me he could barely hop on the sore leg. The pain Phil was experiencing was so bad that Phil had unwillingly ceased running ten days prior to his initial appointment.

Assessment and imaging of Phil's injured hip revealed a stress fracture of the femoral neck (of the hip). On questioning, Phil revealed that the 140 kilometres he had been running each week represented almost double the volume of running that he had previously competed when preparing for previous marathons. Phil confessed that he had not been scheduling in any rest days to his program, and furthermore, by his own admission, he was running too fast during what should have been his slow recovery runs.

I explained to Phil that in essence he had failed to recognise the 'power of rest'. Phil, unfortunately, missed out on making it to the start line of his marathon; however, he has since made a successful and so

Case study: Phil (continued)

far injury-free return to running. Phil required eight weeks off running in order to let the stress fracture of the femoral neck heal. He returned to running in a staged and progressive manner. Phil's rehabilitation included each of the four other steps outlined in the previous four chapters.

Phil now appreciates the importance of rest days and rest sessions and, in his own words he is 'a better runner for the tough lesson learnt: rest matters!'

Putting it
all together

Congratulations on finishing this book.

I believe that every runner, irrespective of their age, shape, or ability level, can and should experience injury-free running. My hope is that you now have an appreciation of the necessary five steps to running pain free, and that you too now also believe that it is possible to run pain free.

Expecting the onset of running-related injuries to develop as a by-product of regular run training is flawed and 'old' thinking. After reading this book, you should no longer expect to develop running-related injuries as a result of your training. An alternate mindset is indeed possible – and, after reading this book, you have hopefully adopted it.

It is time to replace the mindset that 'injury is inevitable' with the mindset of 'I can now run pain and injury free' and subsequently faster. Ideally, this mindset will become your default thinking – *I can and will run injury free and faster!*

It is both the knowledge and implementation of the five steps outlined in this book that will injury 'proof' your running body. It is important to sequentially implement each of the five steps. Each step builds on the previous step, so the best outcomes will be achieved by working from step 1 (discovering your running body), through to step 5 (the power of rest).

This five step method has worked for the thousands of runners I have consulted with over the last eight years of my clinical practice – it's tried and tested and, best of all, offers a proven solution.

What happens next is now up to you. There is always resistance to any place worth going and perhaps you are feeling this resistance to take action.

I encourage you to start with step 1. Take the running screening template (provided in the appendix) to a physiotherapist that 'gets' the rationale of my five step method. This physiotherapist will need to adopt and share the same underpinning philosophy, that all runners are able to run injury free and faster. From step 1 you can then proceed to step 2 – running with great technique, before working your way through the implementation of steps 2 to 5.

If your physiotherapist does not share the philosophy that everyone can run pain and injury free, I suggest you keep looking until you find a physiotherapist who does. It's imperative that you align yourself with someone who shares the running pain- and injury-free philosophy and mindset.

I recently saw firsthand the life-giving benefits of running, when a close friend and client survived what should have been a fatal heart attack. It was only my friend's fitness, developed courtesy of regular running training, which gave him the buffer he needed to survive the heart attack. Decades earlier, this very runner's father had been a victim of a fatal heart attack while in his middle years. Doctors credited my friend's running fitness as his lifeline.

This same runner, who recently passed the one-year anniversary since his heart attack, had, just 18 months earlier, been on the verge of despair after a series of ongoing injuries had robbed him of the ability to run train with consistency. The injuries had my friend questioning whether it was indeed even possible to run pain and injury free. Sound familiar?

He was exposed to the five steps of injury-free and faster running that you have just read. As a result, he discovered new-found levels of enjoyment from what has become uninterrupted and consistent running training, courtesy of the five steps resulting in fewer injuries. Even better is that my friend now enjoys pain-free running at faster times than he had previously experienced, before he discovered and implemented the five step method of running pain free.

My friend now reflects on the fact that running literally saved his life. If I can be so bold, your life, your fitness, and your health are dependent on you now implementing what you have just learnt. In the words of Anne Rice:

Vision without action is a nightmare.

So don't just put this book down. Take action – start now!

Yours in running and great health,

Brad Beer

What now?

1   I would love to hear from you and learn of your journey and progress towards enjoying pain- and injury-free running. Feel free to email me at b.beer@pogophysio. com.au.

2   Follow socially:

Twitter: @Brad_Beer
@pogophysio
Web: www.pogophysio.com.au
www.bradbeer.com.au

3   Attend an in-person RUN101 Running Workshop, www.pogophysio.com.au/run-workshops.

4   Post a photo of yourself holding this book in your running gear (with a big thumbs-up) on social media (Instagram, Facebook, or Twitter) using the hashtag #runpainfree.

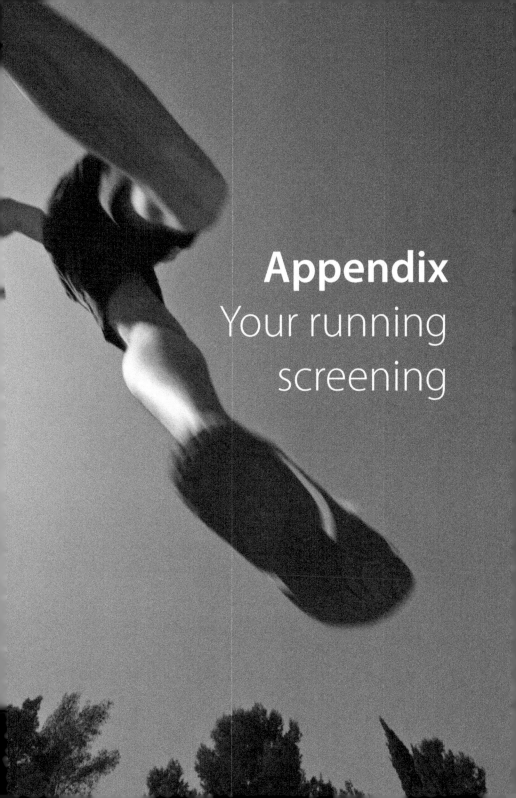

Appendix
Your running
screening

Test*	Your measure	Goal measures	Strategies to improve**	Comments
Calf muscle length (Knee to wall test)	Left side: _____ cm Right side: _____ cm	10 cm hypomobile runners 15 cm hypermobile runners	Calf stretching	This test determines calf muscle 'length'. If calves are tight, they will limit a runner's ability to get the most propulsion out of the calves, and also lessen the effectiveness of the Achilles tendon in performing its shock-absorbing role. Tight calves will also add excessive loads through the knee, ankle, and feet, which can heighten injury risk.
Quadriceps length (Prone knee bend test)	Left side: _____ cm from bottom Right side: _____ cm from bottom	Heels touch bottom (0-cm gap) for hypermobile runners Heels fewer than 5 cm from bottom for hypomobile runners	Quadriceps stretching	Tight quadriceps will pull a runner's pelvis into an 'anterior' or forward-tilted position. This will result in the bottom 'poking out', making a runner look like they are 'sitting in a chair'. Tight quads will also add excessive loads through the knees, which can heighten injury risk.
Hamstrings length (Straight leg raise test)	Left side: _____ degrees Right side: _____ degrees	80 degrees for both hypermobile and hypomobile runners	Hamstring stretching	Tight hamstrings will pull a runner's pelvis into a 'posterior' or backward-tilted position. This will result in the lower back experiencing excessive forces and loads. Tight hamstrings will also add excessive loads through the knees, which can heighten injury risk.

Test*	Your measure	Goal measures	Strategies to improve**	Comments
Hip flexor length (Thomas Test)	Left side: Thigh angle relative to the ground: neutral (OK), hinged (tight), below 90° (good) Right side: Thigh angle relative to the ground:	Hypomobile runners: thigh angle parallel to the ground Hypermobile runners: thigh angle below the horizontal	Hip flexor stretching	Tight hip flexors (as with tight quads) will pull the pelvis into an 'anterior' or forward-tilted position. This will have the same effects as tight quadriceps, but in addition will significantly increase the risk of a runner experiencing lower back pain.
Thoracic spine mobility (Combined elevation test)	_____ degrees	Hypomobile and Hypermobile runners: −10 degrees: very stiff spine, poor range 0 degrees: 'safe' score >5 degrees: mobile spine, good range	Thoracic extension with ½ foam roller	Having a stiff thoracic spine results in an increased likelihood of a runner developing neck, shoulder, or lower back pain. Being able to extend the thoracic spine and run 'tall' is a hallmark of great running technique (as opposed to running with a 'stooped' or 'slouched' upper body posture.)

Test*	Your measure	Goal measures	Strategies to improve**	Comments
Hip stability (Single-leg squat control test)	Left side: Alternate hip drop: Y/N Collapsing inwards of squat leg: Y/N Right side: Alternate hip drop: Y/N Collapsing inwards of squat leg: Y/N	No alternate hip drop (i.e. no angling of the pelvis) and no collapsing inwards of the knee of the squatting leg	Hip stability exercises	This test detects 'core and hip stability' of the pelvis/trunk. It mainly tests the strength and activation of the gluteus medius and maximus muscles. A runner requires stability and strength of the hip and core muscles in order to decrease injury risk, and to also provide a platform for efficient and great technique running.
Hip stability (Hip active external rotation test)	Left side: _____ degrees Right side: _____ degrees	40 degrees for both hypomobile and hypermobile runners	Hip stability exercises	This test detects 'core and hip stability' of the pelvis/trunk. It tests the activation of the hip external rotator muscles. Sound activation and strength of the hip external rotator muscles will reduce the collapsing inwards of the leg on single-leg squat testing and also when running. This will in turn reduce the loading of lower limb structures and decrease injury risk. It will also promote better technique and, therefore, faster and more efficient running.

Test*	Your measure	Goal measures	Strategies to improve**	Comments
Core stability (Side bridge endurance hold test)	Left: _____ (seconds) Right: _____ (seconds)	Hypermobile and hypomobile runners: 45 secs (OK) 60 secs (good) >90 secs (very good) >120 secs (outstanding)	Core stability exercises	This test assesses 'core and hip stability' of the pelvis/trunk. It tests the strength and endurance of the 'side muscles' of the trunk (the obliques, back extensors and gluteus medius). Sound activation and strength of these muscles will aid in minimising sideways collapsing of the hips. Sideways collapsing becomes particularly problematic as a runner fatigues. Excessive collapsing will both slow a runner down and heighten their chance of injury.

*   See www.pogophysio.com.au/book-resources for demonstrations of these tests being performed.

** See www.pogophysio.com.au/book-resources for demonstrations and instruction on performing the required exercises.

References

Chapter 3

1   Australian Bureau of Statistics (ABS). 'Participation in Sport & Physical Recreation, Australia 2011–2012'.

2   ibid

3   Running USA. *2014 State of the Sport*. Part 3: Race Trends.

4   Scott Leitch. 'Hong Kong Marathon fills 30,000 spots in four hours, crashes servers'. *Canadian Running*. http://runningmagazine.ca/hong-kong-marathon-fills-30000-spots-in-four-hours-crashes-servers/ 13 November 2013.

5   Jeanette Wang. 'Marathon running is becoming popular on the mainland'. *South China Morning Post*. http://www.scmp.com/lifestyle/health/article/1450844/marathon-running-becoming-popular-mainland/ 18 March 2014.

6   ASICS *Reasons to Run* Survey 2009.

7   Running USA. *2013 State of the Sport*. Part II: Running Industry Report. http://www.runningusa.org/state-of-sport-2013-part-II?returnTo=annual-reports/ 26 June 2013.

8   Running USA, op cit

9   ibid

10 ibid

11 ASICS op cit

12 ibid

13 ibid

14   ASICS *Reasons to Run* Survey 2009.

15   Lee DC, Pate RR, Lavie CJ, Sui X, Church TS, Blair SN. 2014. 'Leisure-time reduces all – cause and cardiovascular mortality risk'. *The Journal of the American College of Cardiology* 64 (5): 472-481.

16   Chakravarty EF, Hubert HB, Lingala VB, Fries JF. 2008. 'Reducing Disability and Mortality Among Ageing Runners: A 21-Year Longitudinal Study'. *Archives of Internal Medicine* 168 (15): 1638-1646.

17   Chakravarty EF, Hubert HB, Lingala VB, Zatarain, E, Fries JF. 2008. 'Long Distance Running and Knee Osteoarthritis. A prospective study'. *American Journal of Preventative Medicine*. Aug 2008; 35(2): 133-138.

18   Konradsen L, Hansen EM, Sondergaard L. 'Long Distance Running and Osteoarthritis'. *American Journal of Sports Medicine*. Aug 1990: 18 (4): 379-381.

19   Van Gent RN, Siem D, van Middelkoop M , van Os AG, Bierma-Zeinstra SM, Koes BW. 'Incidence and determinants of lower extremity running injuries in long distance runners: a systematic review'. *Br J Sports Med*. March 2007: 47: 469-480.

20   Van Middlekoop M, Kolkman J, Van Ochten J, et al. 'Prevalence and incidence of lower extremity injuries in male marathon runners'. *Scan J Med Sci Sports*. Apr 2008: 18 (20) 140-4.

21   van Mechelen M. 'Running Injuries. A review of the epidemiological literature'. *Sports Med*. Nov 1992: 14 (5): 320-35.

22   McKearn KA, Manson NA, Stanish WD. 'Musculoskeletal injury in the masters runners'. *Clin J Sports Med*. 2006: 16: 149.

23   Fredericson M, Misra AK. 2007. 'Epidemiology and aetiology of marathon running injuries'. *Sports Med*. 2007: 37 (4-5): 437-9.

24   Dias Lopes A, Pena Costa LO, Saragiotto BT, Yamato TP, Adami F, Verhagen E. 'Musculoskeletal pain is prevalent among recreational runners who are about to compete: an observational study of 1049 runners'. *J Physiotherapy*. 2011: 57: 179-182.

25   Van Middlekoop M, Kolkman J, Van Ochten J, et al. op cit

Chapter 4

1   van Mechelen M. 'Running Injuries. A review of the epidemiological literature'. *Sports Med.* Nov 1992: 14 (5): 320-35.

2   Christie Aschwanden. 'The Big 7 Body Breakdowns: How to avoid (and recover from) the most common running injuries'. *Runner's World.* http://www.runnersworld.com/health/big-7-body-breakdowns/ 3 February 2011.

3   Van Gent RN, Siem D, van Middelkoop M , van Os AG, Bierma-Zeinstra SM, Koes BW. 'Incidence and determinants of lower extremity running injuries in long distance runners: a systematic review'. *Br J Sports Med.* March 2007: 47: 469-480.

4   'Plantar Fasciitis'. *Runner's World.* http://www.runnersworld.co.za/injury-prevention/treatment-room/plantar-fasciitis/ 28 June 2011.

5   Taunton JE, Ryan MB, Clement DB, McKenzie DC, Lloyd-Smith DR, Zumbo BD. 'A retrospective case-control analysis of 2002 running injuries'. *Br J Sports Med.* 2002; 36(2):95-101.

6   Lopes AD, Hespanhol Junior LC, Yeung SS, Pena Costa LO. 'What are the main running-related musculoskeletal injuries? A systematic review'. *Sports Med.* 2012: 42 (10): 891-905.

7   Fredericson M, Wolf C. 'Iliotibial band syndrome in runners'. *Sports Med.* May 2005: 35 (5): 451-459.

8   Wilder, RP, Sethi S. 'Overuse injuries: tendinopathies, stress fractures, compartment syndrome, and shin splints'. *Clin Sports Med.* 2004: (23): 55-81.

9   Christie Aschwanden. op cit

10 ibid

11 Taunton JE, Ryan MB, Clement DB, McKenzie DC, Lloyd-Smith DR, Zumbo BD. op cit

Chapter 5

1   K. J. Murray and P. Woo. 'Benign joint hypermobility in childhood'. *Rheumatology*. http://rheumatology.oxfordjournals.org/content/40/5/489. long/ Vol 40, Iss 5, pp.489–491.

Chapter 6

1   A. Lucia, J. Olivan, J.Bravo, M. Gonzalez-Freire, and C. Foster. 2007. 'The key to top-level endurance running performance: a unique example'. *British Journal of Sports Medicine*, vol 42, pp.172–174.

2   ibid

3   ibid

4   'ChiRunning'. Wikipedia. http://en.wikipedia.org/wiki/ChiRunning. Accessed 8 October 2014.

5   Heiderscheit, BC, Chumanov, ES, Michalski, MP, Christa, MW, Ryan, MB. 2011. 'Effects of step rate manipulation on joint mechanics during running'. *Med Sci Sports Exerc*, 43 (2): 296–302.

6   Diebal, R, Gregory, R, Alitz, C, Gerber, P. 2011. 'Effects of forefoot running on chronic exertional compartment syndrome: a case series'. *Int J Sports Physical Therapy*, 6 (4): 312–318.

7   Heiderscheit, BC, Chumanov, ES, Michalski, MP, Christa, MW, Ryan, MB. op cit

8   Taunton, J, Ryan, M, Clement, D, McKenzie, C, Lloyd-Smith, R, Zumbo, B. 2002. 'A retrospective case control analysis of 2002 running injuries'. *Br J Sports Med*. 36 (2): 95–101.

9   Stathopulu, E, Baildam, E. 2003. 'Anterior knee pain: a long term follow-up'. *Rheumatology*, 42 (2): 380–382.

10 Edwards, WB, Taylor D, Rudolphi, TJ, Gilletee, JC, Derrick, TR. 2009. 'Effects of stride length and running mileage on a probabilistic stress fracture model'. *Med Sci Sports Exerc*, 41: 2177–84.

11 Dallam, GM, Wilber RL, Jadelis, K, Fletcher, G, Romanov, N. 2005. 'Effect of global alteration of running technique on kinematics and economy'. *J Sports Sciences*, 23(7), 757–764.

12 Larson, P, Higgins, E, Kaminski, J, Decker, T, Preble, J, Lyons, D, McIntyre, K, Normile, A. 2011. 'Foot strike patterns of recreational and sub-elite runners in a long distance road race'. *J Sports Sc*, 29(15): 1665–73.

13 Daoud, A, Geissler, G, Wang, F, Saretsky J, Daoud Y, Lieberman D. 2012. 'Foot strike and injury rates in endurance runners: a retrospective study'. *Med Sci Sports Exer*, 44 (7): 1325–34.

14 ibid

15 Magill, P. 2014. 'Recoil: running's superpower: find free energy for your stride with these six training exercises'. *Running Times*. http://www.runnersworld.com/race-training/recoil-runnings-superpower. Accessed 8 October 2014.

Chapter 7

1 Franz, JR, Corbyn M, Wierzbinski I, Kram R. 2012. 'Metabolic cost of running barefoot versus shod: is lighter better?'. *Med. Sci. Sports Exerc.* 44 (8) pp.1519–1525.

2 Ryan, M, Elashi, M, Newsham-West, R, Taunton, J. 2013. 'Examining injury risk and pain perception in runners using minimalist footwear'. *Br J Sports Med*. Dec, doi:10.1136/bjsports-2012-092061

3 Heiderscheit, BC, Chumanov, ES, Michalski, MP, Christa, MW, Ryan, MB. 2011. 'Effects of step rate manipulation on joint mechanics during running'. *Med Sci Sports Exerc*. 43 (2): 296–302.

4   Richards, CE, Magin, PJ, Callister, R. 2009. 'Is your prescription of distance running shoes evidence based?'. *Br J Sports Med.* 43: 159–162.

5   Taunton JE, Clement DB, McNicol K. 1982. 'Plantar fasciitis in runners'. *Can J Appl Sport Sci.* 7 (1): pp.41–44.

6   Viitasalo JT, Kvist M. 1983. 'Some biomechanical aspects of the foot and ankle in athletes with and without shin splints'. *Am J Sports Med.* May–June; 11 (3): pp125–30.

7   Nigg, BM. 2001. 'The role of impact forces and foot pronation: a new paradigm'. *Clin J Sport Med.* 11 (1): pp.2–9.

8   ibid

9   Tam, N, Wilson, JA, Noakes, TD, Tucker, R. 2013. 'Barefoot running: an evaluation of current hypothesis, future research and clinical implications'. *Br J Sports Med.* (0) pp: 1–8/bjsports-2013-092404.

10   ibid

11   Tam, N, Wilson, JA, Noakes, TD, Tucker, R. op cit

12   Nagel, A, Fernholz, F, Kibele, Rosenbaum, D. 2008. 'Long distance running increases plantar pressures beneath the metatarsal heads: a barefoot walking investigation of 200 marathon runners'. *Gait Posture.* 27, pp.152–155.

13   Azevedo, LB, Lambert MI, Vaughan CL, O'Connor, CM, Schwellnus, MP. 2009. 'Biomechanical variables associated with Achilles tendinopathy in runners'. *Br J Sports Med.* 43: 288–292.

14   Richards, CE, Magin, PJ, Callister, R. op cit

15   Payne, C. 2013. 'What is the ideal "drop" for a running shoe?'. Run Research Junkie. http://www.runresearchjunkie.com/what-is-the-ideal-drop-for-a-running-shoe. Accessed 20 October 2014.

16   Roy, JP, Stefanyshyn, DJ, 2006. 'Shoe midsole longitudinal bending stiffness and running economy, joint energy, and EMG'. *Med. Sci. Sports Exerc.* 38 (3), pp.562–569.

Chapter 8

1   Sato, K, Mokha, M. 2009. 'Does core strength training influence running
     kinetics, lower-extremity stability, and 5000m performance in runners?'.
     J Strength and Conditioning Research. 23 (1): 133–140.

2   Ferber, R, Noehren, B, Hamill, J, Davis, I. 2010. 'Competitive female
     runners with a history of iliotibial band syndrome demonstrate atypical
     hip and knee kinematics'. *J Orthop Sports Phys Ther*. 40: 52–8.

3   Noehren, B, Davis, I, Hamill, J. 2007. 'ASB clinical biomechanics award
     winner 2006: prospective study of the biomechanical factors associated
     with iliotibial band syndrome'. Clin Biomech (Bristol, Avon). 22: 951–6.

4   Souza, RB, Powers, CM. 2009. 'Differences in hip kinematics, muscle
     strength, and muscle activation between subjects with and without
     patellofemoral pain'. *J Orthop Sports Phys Ther*. 39: 12–9.

5   Powers, CM. 2010. 'The influence of abnormal hip mechanics on knee
     injury: a biomechanical perspective'. *J Orthopd. & Sports Phys. Ther*. 40 (2):
     42–51.

6   Ireland, ML, Wilson, JD, Ballaynte, BT, Davis, IM. 2003. 'Hip strength
     in females with and without patellofemoral pain'. *J Orthop. Sports Phys.
     Ther*. 33: 671–676.

7   Leetun, DT, Ireland, ML, Willson, JD, Ballaynte, BT, Davis, IM. 2004.
     'Core stability measures as risk factors for lower extremity injury in
     athletes'. *Med. & Sci. in Sports & Ex*. 36 (6): 926–34.

8   Tucker, R. 2007. 'Running economy part III: training techniques to
     improve economy (or should that be performance?)'. The Science of Sport
     (website). http://sportsscientists.com/2007/12/running-economy-part-
     iii/. Accessed 20 October 2014.

9   Radin, EL. 1986. 'Role of muscles in protecting athletes from injury'.
     Acta Med Sc and Suppl. 711: 143–7.

Chapter 9

1   Committee on Sleep Medicine and Research. 2006. 'Sleep Disorders and Sleep Deprivation: An Unmet Public Health Problem'. The Institute of Medicine. April 4, press release, http://www.iom.edu/CMS/3740/23160/33668.aspx.

2   Colbert, D. 2007. *The Seven Pillars of Health: The Natural Way to Better Health for Life*. Siloam; p.46.

3   ibid

4   ibid

5   ibid

6   Becker, B, Binkley, T, Vukovich, M, Beare. 2007. 'Volumetric bone mineral density and bone size in sleep deprived individuals'. *Osteop Int.* 18; 93–99.

7   Xiaohua, F, Xinyu, Z, Lu, H, Jiang, F, Xiaoguang, M, Shankuan, Z. 2011. 'Association between sleep duration and bone mineral density in Chinese women'. *Bone.* 49 (5); pp.1062–1066.

8   Dias Lopes, A, Pena Costa, LO, Saragiotto, BT, Yamato, TP, Adami, F, Verhagen, E. 2011. 'Musculoskeletal pain is prevalent among recreational runners who are about to compete: an observational study of 1049 runners'. *AusJPhys.* 57: 179–182.

9   'Cortisol'. Wikipedia. http://en.wikipedia.org/wiki/Cortisol#Normal_levels. Accessed 19 October 2014.

Lightning Source UK Ltd.
Milton Keynes UK
UKOW01f2031290817
308205UK00011B/654/P